MAP INTERPRETATION

MAP INTERPRETATION

BY

G. H. DURY, M.A., Ph.D., F.G.S.

Lecturer in Geography, Birkbeck College
(University of London)

WITH A FOREWORD BY

A. E. MOODIE, B.A., Ph.D.

Reader in Geography, Birkbeck College
(University of London)

AND A CONTRIBUTION BY

H. C. BROOKFIELD, B.A., Ph.D.

LONDON
SIR ISAAC PITMAN & SONS, LTD.
PITMAN HOUSE, PARKER ST., KINGSWAY, W.C.2
BATH   MELBOURNE   JOHANNESBURG

First published 1952
Reprinted 1957
Second edition 1960

©

G. H. Dury
1960

MADE IN GREAT BRITAIN AT THE PITMAN PRESS, BATH
Fo—(E.5196)

FOREWORD

THE statement that maps are the geographer's tools has been repeated so often that it is in danger of becoming a platitude: yet there can be no doubt as to the validity of its meaning. It is difficult, if not impossible, to imagine a course of geographical study being followed successfully without constant recourse to maps of a wide variety in type and scale. Ability to use these maps is an essential requirement of all geographers, but it is not an easy skill to acquire. After more than twenty years of experience in teaching undergraduates, I am fully aware of the difficulties which confront the uninitiated in map interpretation. There is a world of difference between a Boy Scout finding his way from *A* to *B* by map-reading and a geographer seeking to illuminate his studies by map interpretation, although the map is a "tool" in each case. The latter requires the ability not only "to see solid" but also to grasp and explain the relationships between all the conditions which the map represents in symbolical form.

Some people seem to have a flair in this direction, but competence can be acquired only by application and frequent practice. Dr. Dury does not claim to have covered all the problems of his subject, but the student who masters the principles laid down here will be well on the way to a mastery of map interpretation: he will have learned the use of his tools in the sense that they are peculiar to geographical study.

Such an achievement will be commendable, but this book also draws attention to a major problem in modern geography. Dr. Dury lays emphasis on the importance of adequate knowledge of physical geography in map interpretation, but he by no means neglects the human aspects. Indeed, the close relationships between man and nature are brought out clearly. This symbiosis, the core of geography, is in danger of being overlooked, owing to the increasing tendency of recent years towards specialized studies. Maps can no more show all the conditions of an area than they can reveal all the relationships which exist in it, but they represent the closest approach to an expression of its wholeness. It follows, therefore, that map interpretation fosters the development of a balanced outlook and its practice is, in consequence, a valuable discipline. When combined with field investigations, as suggested by Dr. Dury, it becomes one of the most rewarding of activities for geographers at all levels.

A. E. M.

ACKNOWLEDGMENTS

I WISH to acknowledge with gratitude the help I have received in preparing this book. My colleagues Miss E. M. J. Campbell, M.A., and H. C. Brookfield, B.A., Ph.D., have read portions of the manuscript, while A. E. Moodie, B.A., Ph.D., has offered constructive suggestions on the whole book. Dr. Brookfield contributed a chapter (XVI) to the first edition. Parts of his material have been incorporated in the corresponding chapter in this edition, where considerable revisions have been made in accordance with changes in map series. The Controller, H.M.S.O., has permitted O.S. material to be reproduced or otherwise made use of in the illustrations; photographs have been obtained from H.M. Geological Survey and from Hunting Aerosurveys, Ltd.

G. H. D.

Birkbeck College,
February, 1960.

CONTENTS

vii

LIST OF ILLUSTRATIONS

LIST OF PLATES

xi

Straight mine eye hath caught new pleasures
While the landscape round it measures.—MILTON

CHAPTER I

INTRODUCTORY

It is an hieroglyphical and shadowed lesson of the whole world.—Sir Thomas Browne

It has long been tacitly assumed that a map interpreter has no field knowledge of the country with which he has to deal; but, now that field-work has come to be generally accepted as an integral part of geographical study, this antique fiction should be discarded. It is clear, of course, that the most extensive and prolonged excursions can sample only a little of even this country, and that only the most fortunate will be able to observe, at first hand, contemporary glaciers, deserts, or tropical landscapes. On the other hand, an impressive variety of terrain is easily accessible from all the great centres of population, so that school journeys, university field-classes, and less formal explorations can exemplify, in the large, much of the material which must inevitably be compressed and generalized in the text-book. Hence it is reasonable to urge that students of geography should become acquainted on the ground with many of the landforms developed in the normal (humid) cycle of erosion, with the leading features of limestone country, with glaciated landscapes, and with shorelines, as well as with a wide range of land-use and settlement forms. It is no exaggeration to claim that every locality has its own opportunities for field study of the most rewarding kind. In due course, then, the interpreter will be capable of bringing knowledge of real country to bear on his problems—not necessarily knowledge of the actual country represented on a given map, but of country which is essentially similar. The value of such an approach cannot be over-stated. It implies the whole difference between performing an abstract exercise and dealing in realities.

Relation of Work with Maps to Work on the Ground

The question of field-work as an aid to map interpretation devolves, in part, upon the difference of scale. On the 1/63,360 maps of the Ordnance Survey, which must be the customary tool for many geographical purposes, a large number of significant individual features are necessarily suppressed. Even though they are represented, they may not be distinctive. The only possible corrective is a comparison, *on the ground*, between the object itself and its appearance on the map. Practice in comparison of this kind will ensure a very high yield of information. The map becomes astonishingly clarified and illuminated by real experience. So true is this, and so partial and unsatisfactory is work with the map alone, that one may insist on the ground itself as the proper place to learn map reading. There are, admittedly, a few excellent elementary texts, which set out to introduce their users to the method of representing country on a greatly reduced scale by means of symbols, and to the manner of transposing the symbols back into words; but, however skilful one may become in this respect, the exercise is valueless unless the symbols are understood in terms of real objects. Thus texts on map reading should be regarded as comprehensive and formal additions to study of the home region with its own maps.

Now the present book does not set out to teach map reading. It is expected that the user will already possess an elementary vocabulary of cartographical terms, and will be able, with some assistance from a key, to perceive the meaning of the several notations employed. We are concerned here, not with the translation of individual items, but with the terrain as a whole. In map reading one learns a new language; in map interpretation one begins to speak it. The reduced scale of the map is no longer merely a difficulty to be overcome as well as may be: it is the means whereby a broad expanse of country can be surveyed at one time. Herein lies the great value of work with maps. They provide a synoptic view and, to the skilled interpreter, reveal the distributions and interrelations with which geography is peculiarly concerned.

Map Interpretation and Map Analysis

Map interpretation, like a great deal of geography in general, involves a synthesis in which complex ideas are deduced and combined from simple ones. This point is worth emphasizing, for maps lend themselves readily to a number of attractive exercises in analysis, and it is important not to mistake the results of these for the results of interpretation. For instance, one might transfer to a sheet of tracing paper the roads, or the buildings, represented on one of the O.S. 1/63,360 sheets. The resulting map would indubitably reveal, with all possible clarity, the distribution in question, but only because all other distributions had been excluded. Interrelations would no longer appear. If two distributions were mapped on a single tracing, for example, those of relief and moorland, the result would be a partial synthesis, the whole of which is provided by the original map. This is not to say that selective mapping has no value. It can, on the contrary, be highly instructive, just because it throws into relief a single distribution which on the more detailed map is obscured. A number of statements in the following text are based on analysis of precisely this kind, but the problem is ultimately one of cartographic representation and of skill in handling the map. In a rather different context, analysis is the correct, indeed the only, method of operation. A number of techniques have already been evolved for treating map information statistically, and their number may well be usefully added to in the course of time. Samples of these methods in their application to the study of landform are briefly described in Chapter XV.

Background Knowledge

In addition to some knowledge of the elements of map reading, the interpreter needs a grounding in physical geography and elementary geology. Within the limits of Part I of this book, where physical interpretation is treated, there is no room to discuss or summarize all the fundamental concepts of this branch of study. It must, therefore, be assumed that the reader is, or soon will be, acquainted, in outline, with the scheme of the normal cycle of erosion. Moreover, the landforms of the normal cycle are likely to be accessible to a majority of students. In the discussion of maps of shorelines, of glaciated, arid, and karstic landscapes, however, rather more explanatory detail has been included, partly because the features concerned offer special problems to the cartographer and, therefore, to the user of the map. Throughout the book, where technical terms necessary in description are introduced for the first time, they have been printed in heavy type, so that one may easily perceive the range of geographical vocabulary required, and refer, if necessary, to the relevant pages of a standard text.

As yet, physical geography is better served in the matter of textbooks than the features of human occupance, which are dealt with in Part II. In the words of Professor S. W. Wooldridge, we as geographers are concerned with land genesis, land quality, and land use. Thanks to the combined efforts of geologists and geomorphologists, the manner of land genesis is sufficiently well understood. Although a formidable body of material still awaits detailed attention, descriptions in general terms and some noteworthy special studies are universally available. Land quality, on the other hand, has long been regrettably neglected, or disposed of in brief and inadequate phrases. This will continue until the rudiments of soil science, the use of soil maps, the detailed investigation of landscape facets, and the factors of microclimatology have been combined in an improved geographical discipline. It is evident, from the beginnings that have been made, that land quality, like land genesis, will in time be accorded a systematic treatment, with its elements clearly stated in an orderly form; but, until then, map interpretation must perforce make do with a minimum of factual information about land quality, and must move almost directly from land genesis to land use. In dealing with land use one is concerned with almost the whole field of human endeavour. On the time-scale of man's history, even of his written history, the cultural landscape is an impermanent and rapidly changing complex of features. Consequently, the problem of interpreting land use, in its widest sense, from maps, is one which involves a large number of complexly related variables. This is why, in Part II, there can be no short list of standard texts for background reading comparable to that suggested for physical study, and why it has seemed desirable to state principles more fully than in the earlier part.

In Part III two special topics are discussed: cartographical appreciation and the analysis, by measurement on maps, of landform. The two chapters are intended for those more advanced students who require to make a comparative study of different map series, or to carry out an exploratory morphological survey, and who will normally have access to a large map collection.

Bibliographical References

Selected bibliographical references are provided at the end of each chapter. They are of two kinds. The first includes a number of the better-known text-books dealing with the subjects discussed, so that the reader may revise, amplify, or extend his general geographical knowledge at need. The second consists of important single papers dealing with individual topics, including a number of specific points which are treated in the main text. It is hoped that in this way statements can be substantiated, if necessary, by reference to the original authority, without recourse to cumbrous footnotes, and that the lists will serve to locate useful material for further reading. It is not suggested, or intended, that the student of map interpretation should read them all. Indeed, the beginner is best advised to defer all such work until he is well grounded in basic principles. Sooner or later, however, he should attempt a modicum of detailed reading, in order to appreciate the direction and scope of current geographical research, and the nature of the ground which he encounters on the map. This is particularly important since nothing has been included in the interpretations but what can fairly be obtained from the map, except where additional notes of the briefest sort have proved essential. Some of the articles cited are, therefore, to be regarded as possible supplements to, and extensions of, the present text.

It will be clear from the table of chapter headings that the arrangement of Part I is broadly similar to that of several text-books of physical geography. This consideration, as much as any other, governed the selection of the maps treated herein; but any selection had necessarily to be a compromise. In addition to illustrating, *within the limits of the sheet lines*, some leading classes of physical landscape, the maps were required to exemplify a variety of settlement, both in respect of density and of form. It was desired, furthermore, to keep the list as brief as possible, on the grounds of expense, and from the O.S. maps to select as far as possible those showing accessible pieces of country. These various factors operated with different strength in different cases. The inclusion of Ingleborough, for example—a piece of country more than once included in books on map reading—is due to its convenient occurrence in the centre of a 1/25,000 sheet. Other things being equal, the precise area chosen is that best known to the author.

Selection of Maps

In accordance with the view that work on maps and work in the field are inseparable, the text which follows relates largely to the maps of the Ordnance Survey on the scales of 1/63,360[1] and 1/25,000. The complete list of maps required is given in the table on page 6.

The total cost of the maps required, with the exception of the last

---

[1] When the first edition of this book was prepared, the then current New Popular Edition of the 1/63,360 Map was used. This Edition is now superseded by the Seventh Series, but the sheet lines remain unchanged, and the older series may still be employed. Sheet-line changes, however, affect the map initially chosen for Scotland (Popular, Sheet 47).

two, which are used here only to illustrate cartographical appreciation, is thus £1 12s. 8d.

The prices given for O.S. maps are the current prices less one-third. O.S. maps required for educational purposes may be obtained direct from the Director General, Ordnance Survey, Chessington, Surbiton, Surrey. Discount is allowed at the rate of 33⅓ per cent for 1/25,000

SERIES	SCALE	NUMBER AND TITLE	PRICE
O.S. (Seventh Series or New Popular Edition)	1/63,360	114 (Boston and Skegness) 144 (Cheltenham and Evesham) 165 (Weston-super-Mare) 167 (Salisbury) 186 (Bodmin and Launceston)	2s. 4d. per sheet
O.S. Tourist Map	1/63,360	Lorn and Lochaber	3s.
O.S.	1/25,000	NC/76 SY/18 SO/00 SD/77 NY/71	2s. per sheet
Survey of Ireland	1/63,360	169 (Sheets 169, 170, 180, and 181, printed as a single sheet)	2s.
U.S. Department of the Interior: Geological Survey	1/62,500	Arizona (Pinal County) Casa Grande Quadrangle	6s.
Netherlands: Topographische Dienst (Topographic Service)	1/25,000	New Series No. 25A (Haarlem)	5s.
Germany: Landesvermessungsamt (Land Survey Office) Nordrhein-Westfalen	1/25,000	4506 (Duisburg)	7s. 6d.

and smaller-scale maps. Orders should be accompanied by O.S. form, O.S. 318, countersigned by the appropriate educational authority. Prices of foreign maps are liable to fluctuate with rates of exchange, and those given should be taken as approximate. Agents dealing in foreign maps include Sifton Praed & Co., Ltd., 67 St. James's Street, London, S.W.1, and Edward Stanford, Ltd., 12–14 Long Acre, London, W.C.2.

NOTES AND REFERENCES

The following may be recommended for background reading—

SIR. C. CLOSE. *The Map of England.* Peter Davies, London, 1932.

F. DEBENHAM. *Map Making.* Blackie, London, 1940.

A. R. HINKS. *Maps and Survey.* University Press, Cambridge, 1942.

H. S. L. WINTERBOTHAM. *A Key to Maps.* Blackie, London, 1945.

The most abundantly illustrated works on map interpretation are undoubtedly—

R. D. SALISBURY and W. W. ATWOOD. *The Interpretation of Topographical Maps.* U.S. Geological Survey, Professional Paper 60, Washington, 1908.

A. GARNETT. *The Geographical Interpretation of Topographical Maps.* Harrap, London, 1935. (Accompanied by an atlas of selected maps.)

In the early years of this century H. R. Mill proposed that geographical memoirs should be produced, corresponding to the Sheet Memoirs of the Geological Survey. A great deal of material additional to that shown on the map would naturally be included, but Mill's essay is nevertheless well worth study in connection with map interpretation—

H. R. MILL. "A Fragment of the Geography of England." *Geogr. Journ.*, xv, 1900, pp. 205, 353.

PART I
PHYSICAL INTERPRETATION

CHAPTER II

PHYSICAL INTERPRETATION: GENERAL

*The form of the land-surface is perhaps the most funda-
mental of all geographical factors.*—WOOLDRIDGE

A STRICTLY analytical attack on the problem of interpreting the physical
landscape from maps will usually prove the most effective. The method
advocated here resembles qualitative analysis in chemistry, or the use
of mineralogical tests by the field geologist, and might indeed be aptly
described as the qualitative interpretation of landscape. Each operation
is carried out in three stages. First, the interpreter works systematically
over the map, identifying individual features, assemblages of features,
and types of terrain. Next, the kind of erosion-cycle in progress and
the most evident structures are determined. Finally, the map is carefully inspected for special features associated with the particular mode
of denudation, but not yet discovered, as well as for evidence of stage
in the current cycle and for signs of sculpture in previous cycles. With
practice, many of the essential facts are perceived at a glance, but
orderly treatment can never be dispensed with, especially if difficult
maps are likely to be encountered.

General Characteristics of the Landscape

W. M. Davis's classic description of the physical landscape as "a
function of structure, process, and stage" embodies the fundamental
principle to be observed, and serves as a basis for a scheme of operations.
It is, of course, quite clear that all three elements cannot be fully interpreted from every, or perhaps from any, topographical map. Nor is a
stereotyped procedure or treatment to be recommended. In some
areas the main interest will reside in a close correspondence between
structure and surface; elsewhere the chief concern will be landforms
developed in one of the special cycles; elsewhere again, the map will
provide striking evidence of erosional forms belonging to a certain
stage of the cycle, or of a combination of forms developed under the
control of more than one base-level. While, therefore, structure,
process, and stage must always be taken into account, they need not be
discussed in that order, and it is frequently desirable to lay emphasis

on one particular aspect. Examples of varying treatment and emphasis will be found in the descriptive chapters which follow.

In order to provide a convenient scale of reference and a guide to orderly interpretation of physique, several lines of reasoning are brought together in the accompanying table. This is arranged, for convenience, in summary form, not as a set scheme of headings under which, in the order given, results should be presented. However, there is no doubt that physical interpretation is most successful when it is carried out systematically, or that the task is considerably simplified when, by the use of some such scheme as this, many possibilities can be at once eliminated. The table should assist the interpreter to identify the kind of terrain represented, to locate critical features, to perceive apparent anomalies, and to test his conclusions.

No attempt has been made to catalogue all the typical or critical features of the various classes of physical landscape, for this would have made the table unwieldy, in addition to usurping some of the functions of text-books of geomorphology. On the other hand, the table is so arranged that the relevant portions of standard texts can be discovered easily from an index, and reading or revision carried out as necessary. If a particular class of landscape is dealt with later, a note is made of the relevant chapter in this book; if not, a reference is given to a standard work which contains the description required.

It is, perhaps, as well to repeat that the table is designed for reference, not as something to be assimilated before interpretation is begun. Its frequent use should lead, in due course, to a considerable economy of time and effort, and to a rapid perception of essential facts. It is meant to assist in relating study of physical geography to the use of maps. Like the rest of this chapter, it is intended to assist in the development of a satisfactory technique.

I. PROCESS

Class of Cycle

What form of the erosion cycle is now in progress?

(i) The normal cycle; or	Systems of perennial streams observed.
(ii) One of the special cycles—	
(a) The glacial cycle	Glaciers actually present.
(b) The arid cycle	Intermittent or absent surface drainage, associated with desert features. (See Chapter IX and the texts there cited.)
(c) The karstic cycle; and, if so, are full karstic features developed, or only the modified forms typical of Chalk country?	Absence of surface drainage and presence of sinks in a region of humid climate. (See Chapter VII and Chapter IV on Chalk country.)

If the normal cycle, does the land bear marks of—

(i) Former glacial erosion? — Corries, glacial troughs, etc. (See Chapter VI.)

(ii) Former glacial deposition? — Drumlins or large terminal moraines. (See Chapter VI.)

(iii) Former marine erosion? — Raised abrasion-platforms. (See Chapter V.)

If any shoreline occurs, what is—

(i) Its class and type? — I.e. whether submergent or emergent, highland or lowland, etc. (See Chapter VIII.)

(ii) The stage reached in the present shoreline cycle? — (See Chapter VIII.)

Erosional and Depositional Features

These should be selected and specified, as required, to illustrate the general argument, and to provide evidence of structure and stage.

II. STRUCTURE AND LITHOLOGY

Lithology

(i) Do the rocks as a whole seem resistant or weak? — Strong relief corresponds generally to resistant rocks, but feeble relief is not confined to weak rocks.

(ii) What evidence is there of differential rock resistance? — In sedimentary rocks, the resistant formations are likely to be limestones and sandstones; the weak, clays.

(iii) Assuming a humid climate, is there any sign of permeable rock? If so, are there definite lines of sinks? — Local absence of surface drainage. Limestone with karstic features. (See Chapters III, IV, and VII.)

Geological Structure

(i) Is there a definite alternation of weak and strong outcrops? If so, the rocks are likely to be part of a sedimentary succession, either—

    (a) Horizontal; or — Structural plateau.

    (b) Uniclinal; or — Eroded into scarpland country. (See Chapter III.)

    (c) Domed; or — When denuded, domes are enclosed by in-facing scarps.

    (d) Openly folded; if so, note arrangement of folds, for example, if off-set or pitching. — Eroded anticlines show in-facing scarps; eroded synclines, out-facing scarps. (See Chapter IV.)

    or

(ii) Is the area one of complex structure, for example, strongly folded or faulted? If so, what structural grains can be identified? and — For example, an oldland. (See Chapters V and VI.)

(iii) What, if any, are the signs of
faulting?
    (a) Full development of fault-block topography;

(For a full discussion, refer to the text-books cited below.)

    (b) Offsetting of scarps;
    (c) Rectilineal structural pattern in an oldland; fault-line scarps.

(See Chapter VI.)

and

(iv) Where the structure is generally simple, for example, uniclinal, what minor structures, if any, can be identified?

For example, transverse folds or faults in a scarpland. (See Chapter III.)

and

(v) What igneous masses occur, if any?

For example, granitic bosses. (See Chapter V.)

and

(vi) If volcanic topography is developed, where are the vents, what lava flows can be identified, and how advanced is the dissection of the cones?

(For a discussion of volcanoes, which are not dealt with in the present work, see the texts cited below.
The fullest treatment is given in *Volcanoes as Landscape Forms* by COTTON.)

III. STAGE

Landscape

(i) If a special cycle is in progress, what is the stage reached?

(For descriptions of the cycle in karstic, glacial, and arid conditions, see the works cited below.)

or

(ii) If the normal cycle, is the landscape—
    (a) Unicyclic? or

I.e. still evolving in the first cycle initiated by emergence.

    (b) Polycyclic?

I.e. comprising features developed in more than one cycle; for example, an up-lifted and partly dissected peneplain, or an approximately mature landscape with the lower parts of valleys rejuvenated.

and

(iii) What is the approximate stage reached in—
    (a) The present cycle?
    (b) Any previous cycle whose landforms can be identified?

} (See text immediately following.)

Drainage

(i) Assuming the normal cycle, as far as can be judged from the map, is the drainage mature or not?

I.e. are the long-profiles of rivers smooth throughout?

and

(ii) If breaks of slope occur in long-
profiles, do they appear—
    (a) Of cyclic origin? or   I.e. knickpoints. (See text immedi-
                                       ately following, and Chapter XVI.)
    (b) Non-cyclic?   I.e. determined by structure alone.
    and
(iii) What is the relation of drainage
to structure?
    (a) Well adjusted;
    (b) Partially adjusted;
    (c) Maladjusted; and, if so,
does the discordance appear to be
due to youth, superimposition,
or antecedence?

Interpretation in Terms of the Erosion-cycle

A few supplementary comments are needed on the subject of **stage**. There are good reasons for separating, under this head, landscape from drainage. Rivers may easily attain maturity while the landscape is still youthful, that is to say, there may be a phase-difference in the respective cycles of landscape and drainage evolution, at a time when relief is generally strong. Again, although many maps readily show the stage reached by the evolving landscape, this fact is commonly overlooked in map interpretation where undue emphasis may be placed on drainage. Finally, it is impossible to tell, by mere inspection of a map, whether the rivers shown are mature or not.

The landscape becomes mature in the normal cycle when all initial forms are consumed, that is, when opposing valley walls meet along the crests of divides. Although not all members of a divide system attain maturity at the same time, it is usually possible to distinguish broadly between those landscapes which do, and those which do not, retain in the crest regions remnants of an initial surface or of an erosional platform produced in an earlier cycle. When low divides are separated by broad, flat-bottomed valleys, the landscape is indubitably post-mature. In practice, various complications arise from differences in rock strength. Furthermore, the problem of interpreting a normal landscape from maps often resolves itself into one of understanding a polycyclic landscape, which combines features produced in more than one erosion-cycle, with the possible addition of the forms of earlier shorelines; but, whatever the complexities, landscape is often more easily interpreted than drainage, for contours show the qualities of relief far better than those of river profiles. Where drainage is incised, it is the *landscape* that has not yet become mature after rejuvenation.

A river is mature when it is graded, that is, when its long-profile is a smooth curve decreasing in gradient from source to mouth.[1] Now a graded state can be satisfactorily demonstrated only by accurate levelling in the field. Very many rivers are in fact ungraded, either because their profiles have never been smoothed into a continuous curve, or more commonly because the profiles have been developed in more than one cycle. When a river is rejuvenated, by a general fall of base-level or by deformation of part of the earth's crust, the new profile developing headwards from the new base-level intersects the old profile in a **knickpoint**. Unfortunately many irregularities of profile, whether cyclic or not, do not appear on long-profiles constructed from contoured maps. Hence the ungraded state of some rivers can be proved only by levelling. All that the map interpreter can do is to discover which rivers, according to his map, are certainly ungraded in the present cycle, by locating marked irregularities of profile.

Note that the form of the profile is the only criterion of a graded state; the presence or absence of meanders has no significance here.

Braided streams can be graded. Again, rivers can begin to meander well before maturity is reached in the first cycle, and, once meanders are incised, their trace can obviously be preserved throughout a series of successive rejuvenations.

Physiographic Subdivision

When the processes at work, the underlying geological structures, and the stage reached in the current and earlier cycles of erosion have been decided as fully as the map permits, the work of description may begin. It is usually necessary to subdivide the area represented into parts which, each with its unifying characteristics, may be discussed in turn, and to illustrate the subdivision by a sketch-map. The method of subdividing must be carefully thought out. When, as in most map interpretation, only small areas are in question, it must nearly always depend on physical differences. Field studies in geomorphology have revealed the basic principle, which is that a great part of the earth's surface may be appropriately described in terms of flats and slopes. A geomorphologist regards the physical landscape as composed of a number of facets, each a slope or a flat, some depositional, others

---

[1] Recent work indicates that a smooth long-profile may never be attained, and that maturity may be indefinable in terms of slope. Obviously irregular reaches, however, remain significant.

reflecting the structure of the solid rocks, and yet others entirely erosional in origin. Once this principle is grasped, a contoured map can be used in drawing boundaries between small contiguous parcels of land, differing from one another in form, slope, aspect, geology, soil quality, and frequently also in density and form of occupance and in surface utilization.

The above statements merely express what has long been practised in map interpretation, and record its sound foundation in morphological theory. As Linton[1] has so truly said, "a predilection for morphological subdivisions may be considered as a characteristic of British geographical method"; but, rather surprisingly, no standard nomenclature has arisen, comprising terms useful in identifying and describing the units of country with which map interpretation deals. The word "region" will not serve; "area" is too weak. In this book the nomenclature adopted is that suggested by Linton (op. cit.), as follows—

Site. The unit of the smallest order; the geographical equivalent of a single morphological feature, such as an individual hillside or a patch of river terrace.

Stow. An assemblage of sites, possessing a geographical unity; cf. the examples suggested by Unstead, the valley stows and the plateau stows of the North Downs.

Tract. A group of stows, again with a geographical unity, but with a higher order of complexity; for example the North Downs as a whole.

Section. A unit of higher order, which derives its unity in part from climate, vegetation, and land use; for example the highland of N.W. France (Armorica).

Province. A group of sections with a fundamental geographical resemblance; for example the Oceanic Uplands Province of Linton, comprising S.W. Ireland, S.W. England and the coast of S. Wales, and the N.W. Highlands of France.

Continental Subdivision. The major unit in the subdivision of a continent; for example the Atlantic Highlands, comprising the extreme west and north of Ireland, Scotland beyond the Lowlands, and most of Scandinavia.

The three highest orders are illustrated in Linton (op. cit.).

[1] D. L. LINTON. "The Delimitation of Morphological Regions." Published in *London Essays in Geography*, edited by L. Dudley Stamp and S. W. Wooldridge. Longmans, Green, London, 1951, p. 199.

Needless to say, interpretation on medium scales will be concerned chiefly with sites, stows, and tracts or parts of tracts.

These terms have a self-apparent value in providing much-needed names for use in detailed physical description, and in bringing some precision into descriptive work. When they are correctly employed, there need be no doubt at any time as to the class of unit under discussion, or as to the order of geographical complexity which it is likely to attain. One might discuss at considerable length the use of physical criteria in establishing major as well as minor geographical boundaries, but Linton's scheme has the indisputable advantage of coherence and of working upwards from the fundamental unit of country, the individual feature. The physical basis of unity in a particular piece of country has been finely expressed by the same writer in these words—

"If in any area the physiographical conditions exist for the production of a particular slope form they are usually rather widespread and examples of that form are likely to be repeated fairly commonly over the area." (Ibid. p. 209.)

Sketch-mapping

In drawing sketch-maps one should aim at representing the principal steep slopes, such as scarp-faces, the walls of wide valleys, or the edges of mountain blocks. When a sketch-map is prepared in this way for one of the O.S. 1/63,360 sheets, the subdivision into stows will have been at least partly effected, although further boundaries may be necessary, for example at the edge of a fen which is bounded by low but better-drained country. Steep slopes are physical features and geographical sites; the boundary between stows is usually to be drawn at the foot of the slope.

Physical interpretation, however, demands more than boundaries. Many significant features must be appropriately symbolized on a sketch-map. If contoured maps were already adequate, other devices for showing landform would be superfluous; but, since contours, however close and accurate, are descriptive rather than interpretative, there is need for a scale of symbols suitable for use in sketch-mapping, such as that given here. (See Fig. 1.) These symbols are already widely used and widely understood. Those for steep slopes are all variants of hachuring, which can be adapted at will for representing scarp-faces developed on a variety of geological formations, the abrupt edges of

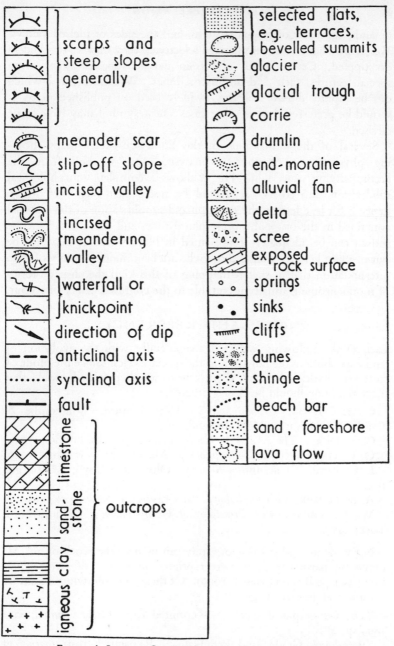

scarps and steep slopes generally		selected flats, e.g. terraces, bevelled summits	
meander scar		glacier	
slip-off slope		glacial trough	
incised valley		corrie	
incised meandering valley		drumlin	
		end-moraine	
		alluvial fan	
waterfall or knickpoint		delta	
		scree	
direction of dip		exposed rock surface	
anticlinal axis		springs	
synclinal axis		sinks	
fault		cliffs	
limestone sand-stone clay igneous	outcrops	dunes	
		shingle	
		beach bar	
		sand, foreshore	
		lava flow	

FIG. 1. A SCALE OF SYMBOLS SUITABLE FOR USE ON PHYSICAL
SKETCH-MAPS

uplands, the walls of glacial troughs, and the sides of incised valleys. Where flats have to be emphasized selectively they may be blocked-in or stippled, Certain kinds of terrain demand special attention to special features, such as drumlins or dunes. When a symbol which can be rapidly drawn is already widely used on published maps, it should be preferred, but in other cases a new symbol may have to be devised.

Several of the illustrations in this book are sketch-maps showing physique, or of physical analysis, using symbols from the accompanying scale, while Fig. 6 shows a complete morphological subdivision into stows. It should be noted that each sketch-map depends for its effect on the selection and simplification of the material contained in the original topographical map, and that the facts to be shown can be adequately represented in black only. It may not be out of place here to counsel those who are beginning the study of map interpretation that in sketch-mapping of this kind the clear austerity of monochrome is usually preferable to the confused gaiety of colour.

NOTES AND REFERENCES

Each of the following works deals generally with the evolution of landscape, both in the normal and the special cycles. Since the mode of treatment varies somewhat from one to another, it is desirable that more than one should be closely studied.

C. A. COTTON. *Geomorphology.* Third Edition. Whitcombe & Tombs, Christchurch, New Zealand, 1942.

G. H. DURY. *The Face of the Earth.* Penguin Books, London, 1959.

O. D. VON ENGELN. *Geomorphology.* Macmillan, New York, 1949.

L. C. KING. *South African Scenery.* Oliver and Boyd, Edinburgh, 1951.

A. K. LOBECK. *Geomorphology.* McGraw-Hill, New York, 1939.

W. D. THORNBURY. *Principles of Geomorphology.* Wiley, New York, 1954.

No student of physical geography can neglect the work of W. M. DAVIS, in particular the papers reprinted in Part II of *Geographical Essays* (Ginn, Boston (Mass.), 1909). Of these, the following should be consulted at an early stage—

"The Geographical Cycle." Reprinted from *Geogr. Journal*, xiv, 1899, p. 481.

"Base-level, Grade, and Peneplain." Reprinted from *Journal of Geology*, x, 1902, p. 77.

Much of the Davisian thesis is now being strongly challenged. For an important summary of opposing views, see—

L. C. KING. "Canons of Landscape Evolution," *Bull. geol. Soc. Amer.*, 64, 1953, p. 721.

The question of geographical subdivision is discussed in—

D. L. LINTON. "The Delimitation of Morphological Regions." Published in *London Essays in Geography*, edited by L. Dudley Stamp and S. W. Wooldridge. Longmans, Green, London, 1951, p. 199.

J. F. UNSTEAD. "A System of Regional Geography." Published in *Geography*, xviii, 1933, p. 175.

Specimens of morphological mapping may be found in—

COMITÉ NATIONALE DE GÉOGRAPHIE. *Atlas de France.* Planches 8, 8A, 9, 9A: Morphologie. (Scale: 1/1,000,000.)

D. L. LINTON. *Watershed Breaching by Ice in Scotland.* Institute of British Geographers, Publication No. 15. George Philip, London, 1951, p. 8. (See especially Figs. 4 and 5.)

S. W. WOOLDRIDGE and D. L. LINTON. *Structure, Surface and Drainage in South-east England.* George Philip, London, 1955.

Techniques of morphological mapping in the field are discussed in—

R. S. WATERS. "Morphological Mapping," *Geography*, xliii, 1958, p. 10.

CHAPTER III

SCARPLAND TOPOGRAPHY

*A most patient and thorough examination of the structure is
made by the destructive forces.*—W. M. DAVIS

MAP: O.S. 1/63,360 (SEVENTH SERIES) SHEET 144
(CHELTENHAM AND EVESHAM)

ON this part of the English Plain scarpland topography is boldly
developed. There can be no mistaking the impressive scarp-face,
rising as much as 800 ft. above the sub-edge country to the north-
west. South-eastwards there is a general, steady descent, readily made
out although the country is considerably dissected. In broad outline,
then, the structure appears simple: the Avon valley has been excavated
in weak, impermeable rocks, while the Cotswolds are based on more
resistant strata, permeable at least in part and dipping gently towards
the south-east. It will be seen in due course that the foregoing statement must be qualified in some important respects, but for the time
being it is well to accept it and to consider, in as much detail as the
map permits, the lithology and geological structure which so markedly
influence relief.

The Scarp-formers

Although the dry valleys of the back-slope indicate permeable rock,
and although the name "down" is given to many hills,[1] this is not
Chalk country. "Chalk Hill" (1326)[2] no more proves an outcrop of
Chalk than "Upper Slatepits" (1032) indicates the presence of meta-
morphosed shales. The texture of relief can be appealed to for
guidance. The short re-entrant valleys or **combes** in the Cotswold
scarp-face are more sharply and deeply cut than the corresponding
scalloped recesses in Chalk, while the contours of the back-slope are
less smooth than those, for example, of the comparable part of the
Chilterns. (See also the following chapter.) The Cotswold terrain,

---

[1] The use of "down" in hill names is adduced, with surprising frequency, as evidence
of Chalk.
[2] Throughout this book, grid references apply only to the kilometre squares.

with narrow, steep-sided valleys and tabular interfluves, suggests a dissected plateau much more strongly than do the swelling undulations of much Chalk country. Discontinuous drainage occurs much more widely here than on the Chalk: a number of valleys are dry only in certain reaches, as, for instance, that of the Dikler between 147303 and 167279, a characteristic which suggests that the rocks of the cuesta are not permeable throughout, at least to a uniform degree. Some sandstones are highly permeable in mass, but rarely develop the localized sinks which cause a stream to disappear; hence it may be concluded that the rocks of the Cotswolds include limestones, which must be mechanically stronger than Chalk in order to support the steep valley walls.

There is some indication in the forms of the scarp-face that the scarp-forming rocks are not homogeneous throughout. The steep descent is broken at several places by benches, most clearly seen perhaps on Oxenton Hill (9631) and in Burhill east of Buckland (0836). The main summit of the Oxenton Hill group, rising to 734 ft., is presumably capped by resistant rock; but a different formation at a lower level would seem to cap the three spurs at 500–600 ft., Dixton Hill (9830), Crane Hill (9630), and the broad shoulder south of Teddington (9632). Similarly at Burhill there is a sharp descent of some 250 feet from the brow of the main scarp to a distinctive flat, which slopes gently to the south in rough accordance with the assumed regional dip. It is, of course, natural to expect that lithological changes should occur in a thickness of some 500 feet of sediments.

The Clay Vale

The strong formations are underlaid by weak rocks, which have been deeply eroded into a strike vale. As stated previously, the weak rocks may safely be regarded as of the clay family; but the lowland tract is not unvaried. The sub-edge country between the scarp and the River Avon is divided into two stows, the Vales of Gloucester and Evesham, by a group of detached hills. The flanks of these hills are so obviously similar in general form and detail to the main scarp-face that they must be geologically similar; the resemblance is emphasized by the distribution of woodland, which is very like that of the main scarp. It follows that the hills are outliers, orographical as well as geological, of the **cuesta,** and that they have survived for some reason while the scarp generally has receded. At first sight there is nothing to explain why they should not also have been destroyed as the strike vale was opened out, but a useful clue may be obtained when a further principle is applied.

Structures

The solution lies in minor structures, which may conveniently be discussed as part of the question of cuesta structure as a whole. It is a mistake to suppose that, in the English scarplands at least, the back-slopes are usually structural surfaces: to this extent the customary simple diagram illustrating elementary accounts of scarpland country is misleading. As a rule, the dip of the strata is greater than the general slope of the ground, so that progressively younger rocks come in towards the foot of the back-slope. Again, in many cuestas minor folds and faults occur, which may or may not be reflected in the form of the ground. Once it is accepted that in actuality a cuesta is likely to possess some internal structural variety, the interpreter is naturally on the look-out for signs. The scarp-face is most likely to repay close study, for its outline may be influenced by transverse folds or faults. In an anticline, for example, the weak underlying rocks will be laid open to attack and the scarp-face may be deeply indented; a syncline which brings down the scarp-former may appear as a projection of the high ground into a strike vale.

The structural pattern of the Cotswold cuesta is somewhat complicated, as intermittent folding took place over a long period, including the time when the sediments were being laid down. Little of the total effect can be made out from Sheet 144, but it is at least possible to see the deep re-entrant valley of the Isbourne above Winchcomb (0228) and that of the Badsey Brook south of Broadway (0937). If these are anticlines, an ill-marked syncline appears to lie between them, with a much deeper downfold west of Winchcomb passing through Cleeve Hill (9826), Nottingham Hill (9828), and Oxenton Hill. Bredon Hill is actually down-faulted, but this cannot be seen from the map. One can perceive, however, that the cap-rock here appears to stand lower than on the main crest of the south: the profile of the Cotswold back-slope, if projected towards the north-west, would pass above the summit of Bredon Hill.

With a little care, the interpreter may further make out signs of earth-movement on a more considerable scale. The map evidence available on this sheet is none too plentiful, but is nevertheless perfectly sound. North of the Avon, a little west of the meridian of Evesham, is a stow of low hill country in which stands Church Lench (0251).

The 250-ft. contour and the patches of woodland draw attention to the steep outward-facing edges, which are appropriate to a denuded syncline. The problem of linking this syncline to the one passing through Cleeve Hill is less important, in the present connection, than the remarkable similarity between these hills and the small cuesta between Eatington (2649) and Loxley (2553). The resemblance extends to the distribution of woodland as well as to height, but lies fundamentally in the details of the scarp-slopes and in the amplitude of curvature of the contours. It looks as if the two stows might be based on a single formation. If so, a strong fold or fault must lie between; for the strong rocks of the Lench Hills occur in the clays of the strike vale and must dip under the scarp-formers of the Cotswolds, but the small cuesta in the north-east is in line with the Cotswold scarp-face. In other words, the north-eastern cuesta is considerably offset down the dip. Such a distribution would be expected if a fault or fold, near the line of the Stour valley, threw down the rocks on the south-western side. In that event one would expect the main scarp also to be offset. In reality certain complications occur, but this map suffices to suggest that Chastleton Hill (2628) may correspond to Ilmington Down (1842) and that displacement of the kind envisaged has taken place. These suggestions are summarized in Fig. 2.

Drainage

The value of interpreting structure before drainage will now be realized. Unless structures can be defined independently, there is no way of telling whether or not the drainage is adjusted. It is an elementary error in logic to assume implicitly that adjustment has taken place, and to use this assumption to define structures. On this view, most of the trunk streams of a scarpland will seem to have become adjusted to structure, whereas in fact many, in the English Plain, are far from being so.

The Warwickshire Avon is often cited as a strike-stream. From the atlas map there seems little doubt that it is; but it has already been noted that transverse structures appear to run across the river, notably in the Lench hills, and there is no alternative but to regard it as superimposed, at least in part. The topographical map provides no clue to the truth, that it has cut into the "solid" rocks through a thick covering of Pleistocene material. Nor is there any sign of the many fans of sludge deposits, which in periglacial conditions spread over the sub-edge plain from the numerous combes.

Terraces of the Avon

Despite these serious limitations, the selected map provides a considerable amount of useful information concerning the later evolution of the Avon system. As always, the interpreter should be on the watch for signs of re-grading in progress. Since the valley bottom is 100 feet or so below the surrounding countryside, it may be assumed that rejuvenation has taken place. The rocks of the Vale are mostly weak, but not too weak to preserve sufficient detail, at a number of sites, to show the manner and the effect of the renewed downcutting. Between Bidford on Avon (1051) and Offenham (0546) meanders appear to have swept freely down-valley, trimming back meander-spurs into straight lines of bluffs, clearing any valley fill, and developing a continuous ribbon of flood-plain. In contrast, the run of the 50-ft. contour in the lobes of Pensham and Birlingham (9444, 9343) suggests slip-off slopes of gentle gradient, which are opposed by undercut slopes at least fifty feet high across the river. Here are certainly ingrown meanders, which have enlarged themselves laterally during incision without migrating downstream to any marked extent. The lobes of ingrown meanders deserve very close inspection for signs of terraces, which are often best preserved at such sites. Although a standard topographical map will never reveal terraces with the clarity of a geological sheet or a special morphological map, something may perhaps be read from the spot heights and the run of drainage channels. Thus, here, spot heights of 81, 79, and 69 ft. are given on the lobe immediately east of Pershore (9646), whereas the flood-plain alluvium stands at only 50 ft. just below Pershore Bridge, 1½ miles downstream. Between the points at 79 and 69 ft. there is a fall of only 10 ft. in ¾ mile; at this rate the river would be reached at 60–65 ft. If these points are on the flood-plain, there must be a pronounced break of slope a little above the bridge. Further search, however, discloses that a patch of terrace is present, for a height of only 61 ft. is marked on the crown of a road, higher up the valley at 999457. Again, the tips of some lobes are cut off by small channels, as near Birlingham, and below the spot height 61 where Lench and Oxton Ditches are named. It is justifiable to suppose that the crescent between these channels and the main stream is part of the flood-plain, whereas on the landward side of the channels the ground stands higher—in other words, that the channels define the edge of the alluvium, acting as drainage ditches for the flood-plain and as catchwaters for ditches or streams flowing towards

the river. Confirmatory evidence is often forthcoming. The field
road through Broadway stops short at Oxton Ditch (cf. the similar

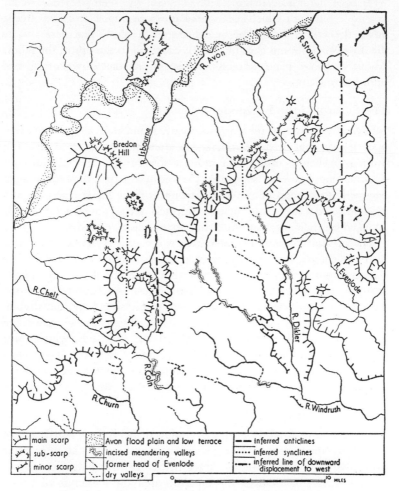

FIG. 2. INTERPRETATION OF PHYSIQUE: THE COTSWOLDS AND
THE AVON VALLEY
(Based, by permission, on Sheet 144 of the O.S. New Popular 1/63,360 Map)

termination of a similar road at 948428). Evesham stands on the lobe of
a notably asymmetric and ingrown meander. On the southern side
of the town, building is roughly confined within the 100-ft. contour,
which curves smoothly round within the loop of the river. On the

south-western, downstream, side of the lobe the river appears to have shifted a little down-valley, leaving a crescentic patch of alluvium with poor natural drainage. The Evesham site seems to have acted as a node, through which meanders have been unable to sweep freely down the valley, for all the evidence goes to show that here and in the downstream loops the alluvium is confined to the tips of the lobes. Above the flood-plain, terrace patches indicate that downcutting has been intermittent.

The Stour and the Evenlode

In the Stour system relief is more varied, and the valley less widely opened than that of the Avon. It has already been inferred that the Stour is probably cutting back along a structural line; but, although downcutting has been vigorous, the meanders have not apparently been able to sweep out an alluvial trough. Note the sharpened spurs near Halford (2645) and below Shipston (2641), which are being attacked on their upstream sides but are as yet little eroded.

The greatest contrast is that between the valleys of the Stour and of the Evenlode, the one with numerous small hills 150–200 ft. higher than their surroundings, the other with a wide, flat floor, which ends abruptly in a steep edge defined by the 350-ft. and 400-ft. contours. This is an erosional scarp. The Stour is pressing back the divide, causing it to **creep** south-eastwards; it has also **leapt,** for the Knee Brook head of the Stour has beheaded the Evenlode which once flowed through the col at Campden Tunnel (Fig. 2). The topographical map can do no more than hint at the former course of events, proof being obtained from work in the field.

Underfit Streams

The action of capture must have reduced the volume of the Evenlode, but capture is not the explanation of underfit. The interpreter notes that in the trace of the river below Adlestrop Station (2526) meanders of small radius are superimposed on windings of much greater size. The small meanders are described by the low-water channel of the river, which appears too small for its valley and is therefore described as a **misfit,** or **underfit,** stream. The implication is that discharge has in some way been greatly diminished. Many writers, following the early work of W. M. Davis, regard underfit as the result of river capture, since beheaded streams are often found in an underfit condition; but Sheet 144 shows that the capturing Stour, as well as the beheaded Evenlode, has meanders of the two orders of size. Each river meanders within a meandering valley, and, in addition, the Avon itself, although much regularized for navigation, displays similar features, for example, in the Birlingham loop. The Coln, which may well have been beheaded by the Isbourne, is no more a misfit than the Avon, which should have been increased in volume by any capture effected. Two useful conclusions may be drawn. Firstly, capture is inadequate to explain underfit, which must be accounted for in some more general fashion. Secondly, it is important to distinguish, in description, between the meanders of the river and those of the valley. It is the lobes of valley-meanders which provide the interlocking spurs so frequently mentioned in introductory studies.

Since underfit streams on the back-slope are not reliable indicators of capture, the contest of streams along the crestal divide must be interpreted with much care. In a tract such as this, where the sedimentary scarp-formers are (as seen above) somewhat varied, and where transverse structures have been identified, a notch in the crest may not invariably be the result of capture. It is quite possible that two streams, one on the scarp-face and the other on the back-slope, have worked headwards along a single line of weakness, approaching the same point on the watershed and forming a col. Consequently the shallow dry gaps, as at Lyne's Barn (0627), may be noted without explanation. There is no way of knowing, from the topographical map alone, which of these are inherited from beheaded streams. Capture appears certain only where, as between the Coln on the one side and the Isbourne and Chelt on the other, the dry gaps are unusually deep.

If in the foregoing paragraphs the limitations of the topographical map seem to have been stressed, the effect is deliberate. It is useless to approach the task of interpreting maps of real country in the hope that structures, landscapes, and the results of human occupance will everywhere be simple. If they were, geographical study would fail to stimulate and many cartographical problems would disappear. There is no point in seeking complexity for its own sake, but the interpreter who is prepared, on general grounds, to find the actuality varied will be best fitted to discover most from the map. It seems particularly appropriate that this initial study of scarpland country, which at first glance appears so uncomplicated and clear-cut, should provide the necessary caution against an over-simple treatment.

NOTES AND REFERENCES

For a general account of the geology, including structure, see—

G. A. KELLAWAY and F. B. A. WELCH. *Bristol and Gloucester District.*
Second Edition. British Regional Geology Series, H.M.S.O., 1948.
(See especially Figs. 3 and 20 for maps of structure.)

F. H. EDMUNDS and K. P. OAKLEY. *The Central England District.*
Second Edition. British Regional Geology Series, H.M.S.O., 1947.

A summary of the orthodox views on the evolution of scarpland
drainage is—

W. M. DAVIS. "The Drainage of Cuestas." *Proc. Geol. Assoc.,* xvi,
1899–1900, p. 75. As stated in the text, this concept is not wholly
applicable to the Cotswolds and the Avon valley.

The capture of part of the Evenlode by the Stour is described in—

W. J. ARKELL. *The Geology of Oxford.* Clarendon Press, Oxford,
1947.

W. J. ARKELL. "The Geology of the Evenlode Gorge, Oxfordshire."
Proc. Geol. Assoc., lviii, 1947, p. 87.

M. E. TOMLINSON. "The Drifts of the Stour-Evenlode Watershed,
etc." *Proceedings of the Birmingham Natural History and Philosophical
Society,* xv, Part viii, 1929, p. 157.

Descriptions of the morphology and drift deposits of the sub-edge
plain occur in—

W. J. ARKELL. *The Geology of Oxford.* (Above.)

W. W. BISHOP. "The Pleistocene Geology and Geomorphology
of Three Gaps, etc.," *Phil. Trans. Roy. Soc.,* Ser. B, No. 682, cxli,
1958, p. 255.

G. H. DURY. "A 400-ft. Bench in South-eastern Warwickshire."
Proc. Geol. Assoc., lxii, 1951, p. 167.

F. W. SHOTTON. "The Pleistocene Deposits of . . . Coventry,
Rugby, and Leamington, etc.," *Phil. Trans. Roy. Soc.,* Ser. B, No. 646,
cxxxvii, 1953, p. 209.

CHAPTER IV

ERODED FOLDS

. . . the shapely figured aspect of Chalk hills.—Gilbert White

Map: O.S. 1/63,360 (Seventh Series) Sheet 167
(Salisbury)

The most cursory examination of this map sheet reveals that most of the ground represented is based on Chalk. The easily recognized assemblage of cartographic symbols and contour patterns stands for a highly typified association of actual features, those of high open downland—a kind of landscape not found throughout the Chalk outcrops but very widespread there. Somewhat paradoxically, a map may allow no possible doubt that Chalk is present, while providing weak or unconvincing items of specific evidence. The best guide to diagnosis is the texture of the country as a whole.

General Aspect of Chalk Country

The most striking attribute of much Chalk terrain is its lack of surface drainage, which in itself proves no more than that the underlying rock is permeable. As in some other limestone tracts, valleys occur although streams are lacking. On the Chalk these dry valleys are found to be distinctively arranged in elaborate branching systems, similar in plan to surface drainage and, with very few exceptions, sloping continuously downwards to their mouths. Dry valleys elsewhere, for example, on the Carboniferous Limestone, are much less regular in form, particularly in long-profile. The smoothly undulant appearance of many Chalk tracts, and the flowing contours by which they are represented on the map are due to a characteristic combination of the dry valleys—the **bottoms**—with the intervening swelling hills. The dry valley systems are generally regarded as having been cut by surface streams in conditions which no longer obtain. The matter cannot be argued at length here, but one may note in passing that the water table has evidently fallen so that percolation has largely replaced run-off. As with other permeable outcrops, springs are to be expected at the boundary of underlying impermeable strata,

31

or in the deeper valleys which have been cut down to the water-table. Streams which head within the Chalk outcrop usually rise well below the upper ends of valleys (cf. on Sheet 167 the River Till, which is shown as rising at Orcheston St. George (0645), over five miles from the watershed and more than three miles below the village of Tilshead). In reality, the sources of streams of this kind are liable to shift up or down the valley, in response to rises and falls of the water-table. An unusual rise may cause temporary streams, called **bournes** or **lavants,** to flow in valleys which are normally dry: in the wet spring of 1950, which followed a wet autumn and winter, many such streams appeared on Salisbury Plain. A "bourne" element may be looked for in place-names, for example, the three Winterbournes (1634, 1635, and 1835) which all stand on the River Bourne.

In some localities the Chalk outcrop is dimpled by sinks, which rarely appear, however, on the standard map. Few streams are swallowed, so that discontinuous drainage, like that of some other limestone tracts, is not to be expected. The combination of many dry valleys with few large localized sinks, which results from the wholesale opening of joint-planes, is a means whereby Chalk can be distinguished on the map from other permeable formations.

Some scarp-faces on the Chalk are remarkably straight, but others are scalloped by short, rounded combes (cf. on Sheet 167 the form of the scarp from Chirton Bottom (0655) eastwards). Combes of this shape appear to have been eroded in the special conditions of a peri-glacial environment and should not, therefore, be looked on as essential features of denuded chalklands, but where they occur they are useful pointers to the nature of the rock.

The evidence so far reviewed suffices, in the main, to prove permeable strata. The special characteristics—the smooth outlines, the dry valley systems, and the general permeability—are those which suggest Chalk, and which, moreover, are all to be discovered from the map of contours and water only. Other evidence, for which one must refer to the full topographic sheet, is almost entirely supplementary in character and secondary in importance. Chalk quarries may be named, as, for example, in "Chalkpit Hill" (2249), but a single example is not always reliable. Similarly the names Broad Chalke (0325) and Bower Chalke (0223) are helpful but not in themselves conclusive. Signs of prehistoric occupance indicate no more than an easily cleared tract of light, shallow soils. Similarly, the little that can be read of present land use provides suggestions rather than facts, and is very far from giving a definite indication of rock type. The interpreter, then, should rely on the forms of the ground and on the texture of the relief to show where Chalk occurs, treating any additional material as tending to confirm inferences already drawn.

Limits of the Chalk Outcrop

It is nevertheless true that certain distributions, for example, that of woodland, may be of use in interpreting the approximate boundaries of the Chalk. One may expect the outer boundary to be associated with a scarp-face, as generally throughout this tract, in which event it is easily fixed: the belts of woodland on rocks beneath the Chalk, as for instance in the upper Nadder valley in the south-west, serve to emphasize (not to demonstrate) the grain of the relief; but, where the Chalk is in part overlain by Tertiary rocks or by Clay-with-flints, the soils are likely to be very different from those developed on the Chalk, and the difference is usually, in fact, reflected to some extent in the occurrence of woodland or heath. The possibility that such deposits may occur deserves to be strongly emphasized, for the chalklands cannot be understood if it is ignored.

On Sheet 167 the bounding scarps of the Chalk tract are seen to flank the Vale of Pewsey in the north, the upper Nadder valley in the south-west, and a small part of the Wylye valley above Upton Lovell (9440). (See also Fig. 3.) One may assume that the Chalk tends to dip southwards and eastwards away from the boundary thus defined. Now within the line of scarp-faces, woodland is extensive only in the east, and on the crest between the Wylye and the Nadder. East of the Avon below Salisbury the woodland is based on impermeable rock, as shown by the surface drainage: from what has been said, it may be guessed that here the Chalk dips under younger, that is, Tertiary, rocks. In the west, however, the woodland occurs on the highest ground, not far from the outer limit of the Chalk tract. It is entirely possible, if not indeed highly probable, that this woodland is underlain by Clay-with-flints, the product of lengthy subaerial weathering of Chalk. Because similar large woods are not found on the crests of other interfluves, it should not be assumed that Clay-with-flints is confined to this stow alone: former woodland may have been cleared for cultivation.

Geological Structure

Chalk having been identified and its limits broadly defined, an interpretation of the geological structure may now be attempted.

Although much of the tract could be described in terms of scarp-face and back-slope, as a whole it is not an area of uniclinal structure but one of folding. This fact may be ascertained in either of two ways: from a synoptic view of all the scarp-faces shown on the map, or from a comparison of inferred dips.

The Chalk scarps which bound the Vale of Pewsey face one another across the low ground and converge towards the east. The same is true of the corresponding scarps of the upper Nadder valley. In each case the forms are those of a denuded anticline which pitches, that is, dies away, eastwards. The extremity of a third similar structure is found in the Wylye valley, in the westermost part shown. If each section of scarp-face is taken as running roughly along the strike, and dip arrows inserted pointing down the back-slopes, it will be found that, for example, the inferred dips are to the north on the northern side of the Vale of Pewsey and to the south on the southern—an anticlinal axis must lie between them. An approximately south-south-east dip near Bratton (9152) opposes one to the north-east at Heytesbury (9242): here a synclinal axis must intervene. In these ways a picture is obtained of a tract of open folding, wherein the axes run approximately east-west and the anticlines pitch eastwards (Fig. 3).

This interpretation is confirmed and extended when the landforms of the anticlinal vales are closely examined. Sub-scarps are found to occur at the foot of the Chalk scarp-faces, that is to say, another resistant formation appears from beneath the Chalk, standing out in a narrow and lower cuesta. South of the Nadder a prominent bench runs from Donhead St. Andrew (9225) to Barford St. Martin (0531), more than a mile wide and clearly demarcated by the steep, tree-clad edge on its northern side. The forms suggest a gentle southerly dip similar to the inferred dip of the Chalk above. Corresponding features occur north of the river, but the bench is replaced by a line of hog-back ridges, here also marked by a line of woodland which runs westward along Wick Ball (0032) and Ridge Hill (9532). The hog-back form signifies a steep dip; or, in other words, the upfold is asymmetrical, dipping steeply on the northern flank and gently on the southern. No sub-scarp is visible in the nose of the Wylye anticline, but it may be at once identified in the Vale of Pewsey. In the extreme west the Chalk and the lower scarps are combined in a single edge, but eastwards of Erdington (9253) the sub-scarp detaches itself and the line of woodland begins near Erlestoke (9654). A line of scarp features is easily traced across the mouth of the Vale, through Devizes, with the help of the woodland symbol which shows where the crowded contours should be looked for.

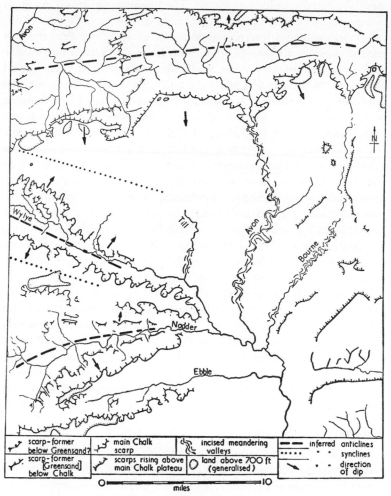

FIG. 3. INTERPRETATION OF PHYSIQUE: THE WESTERN PART OF
SALISBURY PLAIN
(Based, by permission, on Sheet 167 of the O.S. New Popular 1/63,360 Map)

The map indicates no more than a resistant formation, underlying the Chalk and similar in respect of dip. One might well suggest that in view of the general concordance of structure it also is likely to belong to the Cretaceous. In the field the outcrop proclaims itself from a distance. The woodland is largely coniferous (not distinguished on the modern O.S. 1/63,360 sheet) and is very dark in appearance, especially in the colder months. The observer is at no pains to recognize the Greensand.

Further structural interpretation is not easy, except that the low ground west of Devizes is seen to be based on weak, impermeable rock—presumably clay. Axes of folding additional to those described are present in the area and affect the relief in varying degree, but, like the faults which also occur, can scarcely be interpreted from the map. It has already been suggested that the impermeable rocks in the south-east may be of Tertiary age, in which event they would occupy a syncline, but the suggestion cannot be confirmed without more evidence. The geological basis of a number of hills in the east, which rise above the Chalk plateau, must similarly remain obscure until the geological map is consulted. Wexcombe Down (2757) attains 876 ft., unusually high for this tract, and well above the crest level of the nearest bounding scarp. The line of hills from Windmill Down (2451) to Quarley Hill (2642) seems to present a scarp-face, marked by woodland, towards the west, but Sidbury Hill (2150), Clarendon Hill (2248), and Beacon Hill (2044) on the other side of the Bourne valley are less clearly defined. The cuesta form is again found in the high ground which runs north-eastwards from Pitton (2131) and swings eastwards near Roche Court (2534), and also in Deal Hill (2526). Since the rock composing these patches of high ground is not likely to be less resistant than the generality of the Chalk, and, since dry valleys are found, it might be that the scarped hills at least owe their form to resistant beds high in the Chalk succession (cf. the South Downs, where two scarp-formers occur within the Upper Chalk).

The Drainage Pattern

It is true to say that in this tract, as in the English Plain as a whole, not every major structure is unequivocally expressed in the relief. All the more caution is necessary, therefore, in an interpretation of the drainage-pattern. If structures are in part unknown, a complete description of the stream systems in terms of dip-, strike-, and scarp-streams is obviously impossible, for it would imply not only that structures are known but also that streams have attained some measure of adjustment. Maladjustment of drainage, due to youth, glacial interference, antecedence, or superimposition, is a text-book common-place, but it is too seldom realized that much of the drainage of the

English scarplands is maladjusted. The effects of glacial interference and of superimposition are widespread—a fact never to be forgotten in map interpretation.

Although the structures on the area represented on Sheet 167 have been imperfectly discerned from the map, it can be stated that the streams are not everywhere adjusted to them. The Nadder and Wylye occupy anticlinal valleys, the Ebble valley may be synclinal, but the Till, Avon, and Bourne flow across the lines of the east-west axes. Now, if the adjusted streams are the older, it is highly improbable that they would have thrown out tributaries across the structural grain: the maladjusted Avon is likely to be the earlier, with the adjusted streams developed as subsequents along the strike of weak rocks. In other words, the drainage appears to have been superimposed on a group of pitching folds, to which it is as yet only partially adjusted.

Wind-gaps in the scarp crest, on the southern side of the Vale of Pewsey at 9251 and 0151, testify to the capture which adjustment involves. The Till and a feeder of the Wylye have been beheaded by the Semington Brook, a tributary of the (Bristol) Avon, draining the weak outcrop in the north-west. The beheaded streams once rose north of the present crestline, as the (Wiltshire) Avon still does. Note that the divide between the two Avons lies on the resistant formation below the Chalk, somewhat east of the crest of the Devizes scarp. The Bristol Avon is gaining ground here also.

Close inspection shows that the Chalk scarps, and the Great Ridge between the Wylye and the Nadder, have even crestlines, higher than 650 ft. O.D. for considerable distances, but not often above 750 ft. This accordance of level suggests that the flat crestal belt has survived from a former more extensive erosion-platform. If so, the cycle in which the platform was produced must necessarily have reached an advanced stage. It follows, too, that the captures recorded in the wind-gaps must have taken place in the present cycle, for gaps produced in an earlier cycle would have been obliterated by planation.

The incised condition of the larger valleys of the Chalk tract proves rapid downcutting in the present cycle, besides incidentally confirming the resistant nature of the rock. Weak rocks could not support such steep valley walls. Interpretation of drainage is somewhat hampered by the numerous minor channels in the valley bottoms, but it is amply shown that the rivers meander within meandering valleys. Since the general problem of valley-meanders has been outlined in Chapter III, further discussion can be dispensed with, but the present examples are well worth close attention if only by virtue of their bold, unmistakable forms. The inner valley of the Avon between West Chisenbury and Enford (1352) describes a great curve, within which the river traces loops of much smaller amplitude. Similar relations are found, for example, on the Bourne below Idmiston (1937) and on the Nadder (9829). It is the valley-meanders which are ingrown, and the spurs between them which have been eroded, that is, sharpened on their upstream sides. Observe, for instance, the three successive spurs in the Avon valley between Upper Woodford (1237) and Newton (1235).

The minor channels mentioned in the previous paragraph are much too regular to be other than artificial: they are the "drawns" of water meadows. Where they occur the valley must be flat-bottomed, and the Avon both above and below Salisbury evidently flows over a winding ribbon of alluvium. From Charlton (1723) downstream the western side of the valley bottom is dry, however. Settlements occur on the low ground and the main road runs along the valley floor. These are signs of a terrace standing higher than the flood-plain, which although not indicated by contours is identifiable by other distributions. One concludes that the downcutting in the present cycle has been intermittent.

Evolution of the Landscape

The several inferences may now be combined in the following minimum sequence of events required to account for the physical landscape as mapped—

1. Folding along east-west axes; anticlines pitching eastwards, at least one upfold steeper on its northern side.
2. Prolonged denudation, producing a surface of low relief. This surface is recorded in the accordant summits of the present Chalk scarps.
3. Fall of base-level, initiating new cycle later followed by further intermittent rejuvenation. It is probably the consequent drainage of this cycle that has been superimposed.

Adjustment of drainage to structure is still incomplete in the present cycle (cf. wind-gaps, beheaded consequents, streams flowing across fold axes).

Dry valleys belong to this cycle, since they are related to the present river system and lie well below the level of accordant crests.

As might be expected, on general grounds, the full sequence is much more complicated, but the outline given here is valid as far as it goes and of considerable value in the understanding of the terrain represented.

NOTES AND REFERENCES

For a general account of the geology, see—

C. A. CHATWIN. *The Hampshire Basin and Adjoining Areas.* Second Edition. British Regional Geology Series, H.M.S.O., 1948.

The geomorphology is discussed, with more accuracy and in greater detail than in the foregoing text, in—

S. W. WOOLDRIDGE and D. L. LINTON. *Structure, Surface and Drainage in South-east England.* George Philip, London, 1955. (See especially Fig. 10 and the accompanying text.)

Certain aspects of Chalk topography are dealt with by—

A. J. BULL. "Cold Conditions and Land Forms in the South Downs." *Proc. Geol. Assoc.,* li, 1940, p. 63.

C. C. FAGG. "The Recession of the Chalk Escarpment." *Transactions of the Croydon Natural History and Scientific Society,* ix, 1923, p. 93.

F. K. HARE. "The Geomorphology of a Part of the Middle Thames." *Proc. Geol. Assoc.,* lviii, 1947, p. 294. (See especially pp. 326–8.)

J. F. KIRKALDY. "Solution of the Chalk in the Mimms Valley, Herts." *Proc. Geol. Assoc.,* lxi, 1950, p. 219.

W. V. LEWIS. "The Pegsdon Dry Valleys." *Compass,* i, No. 2, x, 1949, p. 53.

S. W. WOOLDRIDGE and J. F. KIRKALDY. "The Geology of the Mimms Valley." *Proc. Geol. Assoc.,* xlviii, 1937, p. 307.

The water meadows represented on Sheet 167 are among those discussed in—

H. P. MOON and F. H. W. GREEN. "Water Meadows in Southern England." Appendix II, p. 373, to F. H. W. GREEN: *The Land of Britain, Part 89, Hampshire.* Geographical Publications, London, 1940.

CHAPTER V

UNGLACIATED UPLAND

Besides the story of the rocks, we may try to trace that of the surface itself.—MACKINDER

MAP: O.S. 1/63,360 (SEVENTH SERIES) SHEET 186
(BODMIN AND LAUNCESTON)

WHEN this area is first inspected for evidence of "structure, process, stage," one immediately notes strong contrasts with the areas of tilted and folded sedimentary rocks treated in Chapters III and IV. The area is a low plateau, undergoing dissection by numerous streams which flow in valleys mostly deep, narrow, and steep-sided. There is nothing corresponding to the broad strike vales or denuded anticlines previously studied, where weak clays formed the basis of wide stows of low ground. Here the rocks are generally resistant. Because of this, and because little progress has been made in the present erosion-cycle, geological structure must in part remain obscure. There are, however, compensations for the interpreter, as will shortly be seen. The processes now at work are those of normal erosion and the shore-line cycle. Because the area bears none of the marks of regional glaciation described below (see Chapter VI) it seems probable that normal and shoreline processes between them have shaped the entire landscape in its present form. The stage reached in the present sub-aerial cycle is that of youth, shown, for example, by the deep youthful valleys and the broad, flat crests which separate them. When the landscape is mature, opposing valley walls will have retreated so far that they meet along the crests of the divides, and the flat tops will have been consumed. It can be seen at a glance that maturity is some way off. Now the subdued relief of the crestal belts is the product of an earlier cycle than the present. The general form of the landscape produced in that earlier cycle would be realized if the existing valleys were filled in. As the existing landscape combines features produced in more than one cycle it is styled polycyclic. The map selected is especially well suited to illustrate the broader features of a polycyclic landscape, and the method of treatment employed in the following paragraphs is intended to exemplify some of the possibilities of interpreting landscape history.

Erosion-platforms

The texture of relief is of two kinds. On Bodmin Moor, which lies north-west of centre and shows up prominently as a blank in the patterns of roads, settlement, and woodland, the valleys are wide, shallow and marshy. Most of the Moor is higher than 800 ft. O.D., with single hills exceeding 1,000 ft. and two over 1,300 ft. This part of the landscape is approaching a senile condition, for the higher hills are mere residuals above a wide, gently sloping plateau surface. In the tracts surrounding the Moor it is the interfluves that are broad and flat. They are separated by the incised young valleys already mentioned.

The contrast of texture corresponds approximately to differences of lithology. China clay pits, for example at 1970 and 1381 on Bodmin Moor, and the extensive workings on Hensbarrow in the south-west indicate that these uplands are based on granite.[1] Other signs of this rock are the many **tors**, where residual piles of joint-blocks have survived the attack of erosion. Tors are usually looked on as the result of subaerial weathering, but it has also been suggested that some, at least, may represent the stacks and islets of shorelines higher than the present. Subaerial processes are chiefly responsible for detaching the boulders which clutter the steeper hillsides of granitic country, and which are indicated on this map by the symbol for rock-strewn ground.

It is clear that the granite of Bodmin Moor stands above the surrounding tracts in virtue of its greater strength, but even here one finds evidence of severe denudation. The very fact that the originally deep-seated granite is exposed at the surface proves that a great thickness of cover has been stripped off in cycles of which no trace remains. The earliest cycle to have left a recognizable mark on the present landscape is that in which the granite has worn down to the surface of low relief noted on first inspection. A closer examination shows that, at c. 850 and 1,000 ft. O.D., the summit of the Moor is a broad, open expanse with slight gradients and correspondingly wide-spaced contours. Such a plateau surface, cut across the granite, cannot

---

[1] One may note in passing that the origin of granite and china clay is wrongly stated in many older geographical texts. The alteration of granitic felspar to kaolin appears to have been a metamorphic process rather than the work of subaerial erosion. The formation of granite is a matter of geological controversy, but it may be said that many authorities regard this rock as incorporating much pre-existing material, rather than as being simply a solidified magma.

be other than erosional. It requires, moreover, a long still-stand to account for the extensive wearing-down of the resistant rock, whether by subaerial or marine erosion. Since planation was nearly attained, it may be inferred that the base-level by which the erosional processes were controlled was not far from the bounding contour of the plateau, say, c. 800–850 ft. O.D. The higher hills overtopping this erosional platform may be residuals from an earlier cycle, for a number of summits are fairly flat, but as a group the hills are too few and too small to justify any attempted reconstruction of a higher platform.

On the flanks of the granite outcrop there is a sharp descent from the c. 850-ft. level, obvious enough on close inspection but much more clearly revealed by generalized contours.[1] Outside Bodmin Moor and Hensbarrow the ground is nearly all below 750 ft., with a general slope coastwards to levels of 200–400 ft. at the cliff-tops. As already noted, the surface is that of a low plateau, broadly preserved on the flat interfluves. It is interrupted at 2757 and 3771 by steep-sided hills, which, since they carry moorland vegetation, may again be granitic, and is undergoing dissection by streams flowing in young valleys. The summit surface, like the plateau of Bodmin Moor, is erosional, not structural. It lies lower than the erosional platform cut across the granite, and is developed across rocks in which the granite is emplaced and which are therefore likely to be considerably disturbed and in part altered. Their structure cannot be discovered from this map, even in outline, for the planation recorded in the summit surface seems to have been complete, and differential erosion in the present cycle has made little headway. There is a hint of structural graining in the river pattern east of Bodmin Moor, where a number of east-west reaches are to be observed, but this fact is significant only if the streams are adjusted to structure.

Former Base-levels

The non-granitic outcrops must have been denuded with reference to a lower base-level than that of c. 800–850 ft. which is thought to have controlled the levelling of Bodmin Moor. Presumably one or more falls of base-level occurred, with still-stands long enough for all the rocks except the granite to be worn down, whether by normal erosion or by the sea. There is, in fact, fair indication on the map of at least one intermediate still-stand. Near Tintagel (0588) a narrow platform occurs between the cliff-top at c. 300 ft. and a marked

[1] See below, Chapter XVI.

topographic riser on the landward side which extends from c. 400–600 ft. O.D. or over. This steep slope might be the line of a former cliff, cut when the strand-line stood some 400 feet above its present level. In general, however, it cannot be claimed that any old shore-lines are well indicated by the map, however accurately they may be defined in the field. The closest scrutiny (on the map) of the immediate coastland will often fail to produce evidence of base-level changes which must have occurred to account for the forms of the valleys. It is so here. The incised valleys are a sound indication that, after the planation which is recorded on the flat intervening crests, base-level fell considerably. As a result the streams were rejuvenated and cut deeply into the erosional platform.

On the high moorland, however, the valleys are not deeply cut: contours cross them at wide intervals, showing a gentle downstream gradient. It is evident that the headward waves of rejuvenation, propagated by the falls of base-level, have not yet reached the head-waters. Somewhere the long-profiles must be broken by knickpoints, where the older and newer elements intersect. The only reliable way to locate a knickpoint is to survey a valley in detail on the ground, for contours are apt to generalize the actual conditions and to that extent to be misleading. However, where rejuvenation has so obviously occurred as it has here, and where the stream profiles are generally steep, major breaks of profile may be revealed to inspection alone. In fact, contours crossing the valleys are significantly bunched, usually a short distance above the boundary of the granite, as follows: on the Inny, from 700 ft. downwards at 1786; on Penpont Water, below c. 650 ft. at 2181; on the Lynher, below c. 700 ft. at 2379; on the Fowey, below c. 600 ft. at 2268 where Golytha Falls are marked; on the St. Neots River below c. 750 ft. at 1871; on the Warleggan below c. 600 ft. at 1470; on the De Lank below c. 650 ft. at 1075; and on another unnamed tributary of the Camel, below c. 650 ft. at 1078. The rough similarity of height, taken in conjunction with the considerable vertical range of each steep descent, suggests that most of these plunges of long-profile are knickpoints related to a still-stand of base-level. They do not appear to correspond to geological distributions.

Denudational Sequence

The polycyclic nature of the present landscape is by this time sufficiently evident. There are, however, additional features to be considered. It will be found when the shoreline is examined that the deep inlets are drowned river valleys (Plate IA). In other words, base-level was at one time lower than it now is, and has risen to its present height.

Unaided inspection has now revealed evidence of the following minimum sequence of denudational history—

1. Unroofing of the granites (very lengthy).
2. Widespread but not complete planation of Bodmin Moor, controlled by a base-level of 800–850 ft. O.D.
3. Fall of base-level to 600–650 ft. O.D.; shallow valleys cut in the granite, non-granitic outcrops severely denuded.
4. Further fall of base-level, probably intermittent with one still-stand detected at c. 400 ft.; non-granitic outcrops further planed off.
5. Relatively rapid fall of base-level to below O.D.; drainage generally rejuvenated and valleys incised.
6. Rise of base-level to present position, valley mouths drowned.

While the refined techniques of morphometry are likely to elaborate this sequence, and field-work is certain to do so, it can be claimed that interpretation on sight, as it were, has made possible a useful genetic description of the landscape represented. Individual valley features can be placed in due perspective against a background of long-continued but intermittent rejuvenation.

Superimposed Drainage

It must be stated at once that much less can be discovered about the drainage system than about the major facets of the landscape. Certain streams, or stream reaches, follow well-defined lines, but it cannot be said how these lines have been determined. The Lynher throughout most of its length, and neighbouring streams to a greater or lesser extent, pursue a south-easterly direction; the Fowey runs westward for about five miles below Doublebois (1964); the Tamar system in the north-east combines east-west with north-south reaches in an approach to a trellis or espalier pattern. Although on general grounds it is possible that some reaches follow structures, there is no means of deciphering the structural pattern. The Lynher to one side of Bodmin Moor and the Camel on the other run in part near the boundary between the granite and the surrounding rocks, but this relationship seems to be accidental, since some of the streams parallel to the Lynher flow across the granite while others rise beyond its limits. In other words, there is little connection between the direction of streams and the geological distributions inferred from the map.

The most useful information comes from a study of the Tamar. From the bridge between Crossgate and Pool (3488) to Greystone Bridge (3680), a distance of about seven miles, the river flows on a valley floor which for this area is relatively wide, and which appears to have been swept over by meanders in their migration down-valley. Below Greystone Bridge the river enters a defile, where the meandering course is deeply incised between steep, close-set walls. In the course of an incision of at least 150 ft. the two meanders which enclose Dunterue Wood and Wareham Wood (3878) have enlarged themselves laterally, slipping off the inner banks and undercutting the outer, but have not shifted far downstream. The meander lobes are as yet little trimmed on the upstream side. This assemblage of forms, which is paralleled at Lamerhooe (3973), indicates a resistant outcrop where the meanders have not succeeded in sweeping out an alluvial trough. The Tamar passes from the weaker to the stronger formation at Greystone Bridge.

It is certain that the river is maladjusted to structure; but it has been concluded from an examination of the landscape that this area was severely denuded in an earlier cycle, during which one would expect the drainage to have become adjusted. A likely possible explanation is that the low plateau into which the Tamar is now incised was covered by a thin veneer of terrestrial or marine deposits, from which rivers were superimposed on to the outcrops now revealed.

NOTES AND REFERENCES

For a general account of the geology, see—

H. DEWEY. *South-west England.* Second Edition. British Regional Geology Series, H.M.S.O., 1948.

Erosion-platforms in part of the area shown on the selected map are described by—

W. G. V. BALCHIN. "The Erosion Surfaces of North Cornwall." *Geogr. Journ.* xc, 1937, p. 52.

Other relevant material occurs in—

J. A. STEERS. *The Coastline of England and Wales.* University Press, Cambridge, 1946, pp. 254–260.

W. G. V. BALCHIN. "The Erosion Surfaces of Exmoor, etc.," *Geogr. Journ.*, cxvii, 1952, p. 453. (See also part of Chapter XV (below) including Figs. 11 and 13.)

CHAPTER VI

GLACIATED HIGHLAND AND A DRUMLIN FIELD

Hills peep o'er hills, and Alps on Alps arise.—POPE

MAPS: O.S. TOURIST MAP, 1/63,360 (LORN AND LOCHABER);
O.S. 1/25,000, SHEET NY/71 (BROUGH)

IN the field, the landforms of highland glaciation are boldly defined, not to say imposing. They are clearly distinguishable from one another, and photograph well. Hence it is easy to become familiar, if only at second hand, with the appearance of glaciated mountains, and to identify on the spot features previously encountered only in the text-book. In a general way the large erosional features also are clearly represented on the map, by means of standard symbols, but certain depositional features show up poorly, if at all.

Landforms of Glaciated Highlands

The fundamental landform of glaciated highland is the **corrie,** the hollow in which snow accumulated and consolidated before moving down-hill. When freshly revealed by deglaciation the corrie is seen to approach, more or less closely, the form of a cylinder, with a shallow concave floor and a precipitous partially enclosing wall. Although there is some difference of opinion about the precise way in which corries are formed, there can be no doubt that the walls are cut back during glaciation, so that corries eat into the high ground. The sheer slopes may be represented by rock-drawing, as on the Fort William Sheet at the flank of Ben Nevis (1671) and along the high ground eastwards to Stob Coire na Ceannain (2674), or by unbroken contours, as, for example, in Coire Dubh (0882) and the nameless corries in 0471 and 1634, each of which is a fine example of the corrie form. The slightest field knowledge of this type of country compels the interpreter to remark also those less noticeable corries which are shown merely by inflected contours, for example in grid squares 9570–9670, and the unnamed corrie on the northern flank of Sgurr a'Mhaim (1666) where the 3,000-ft. contour runs near the foot of the headwall.

In geography the term **tarn** is applied exclusively to corrie lakes.

They occupy shallow basins liable to infilling by peat, downwash, and the coarse scree weathered off the corrie walls. Some have already been drained as the effluent stream has cut down; and, since an enclosed basin was not formed in every corrie, in a given tract of glaciated highland tarns may be uncommon, as they are here. Those which occur are instructive. There are four between Binnein Mor (2166) and Binnein Beg (2267), of which the largest draws attention to a well-marked but shallow corrie. In Coire Leis, on the northern side of Ben Nevis, one single tarn and a group of three indicate what can also be read from other detail, i.e. that Coire Leis is composite. It is, in fact, a short glacial trough, with corries running together along the sides and at the head.

Where high ground is scalloped by encroaching corries, **biscuit-board topography** results. In this tract very little remains of a pre-glacial plateau surface, but a limited amount of subdued country at a high level is to be observed on the divide running northwards through Aonach Beg (1971) and Aonach Mor (1973). If glaciation goes on long enough, neighbouring corries merge into one another. A pair of headwalls on opposite sides of a divide, or a pair of juxtaposed side-walls, intersect in an **arête** (knife-edge ridge). Three or four opposing headwalls intersect in a sharp peak or **horn,** of which the Matterhorn is the type. It is rather remarkable that in the glaciated highlands of Britain the true horn is rare, while many ridges between adjacent corries have not been completely sharpened into *arêtes*. In the tract of the Grampians represented here, the highest summits and the crests of ridges are generally narrow, but nevertheless preserve rounded not sharpened forms. From Stob Coire Easain (2372) to Stob Coire na Ceannain (2674) the forms of the crests are entirely comparable to the subdued relief noted on Aonach Beg and Aonach Mor a few miles to the west, except that here less of the crestal belt has survived. On the southern side of Ben Nevis itself, the relief is comparatively feeble above c. 4,000 ft., with little beyond a field of riven blocks to suggest frost-action. It would seem that, in some parts of the area mapped on this sheet, glacial processes just failed to destroy completely the pre-glacial topography.

During glaciation the corries were the headward catchment areas of valley glaciers. Small tongues of ice from the corries coalesced into great streams moving in U-shaped troughs. If corries are the funda-mental landforms of a glaciated highland, **glacial troughs** are the most distinctive, with their straight reaches and angular plan, steep sides, truncated spurs, hanging tributary troughs, and ribbon lakes (Plate IB). Their long-profiles, despite some alluvial fill, are characteristically irregular in contrast to the smoother long-profiles of rivers. Most of these characteristics are sufficiently apparent on the contoured map, except perhaps for truncated spurs, which although numerous

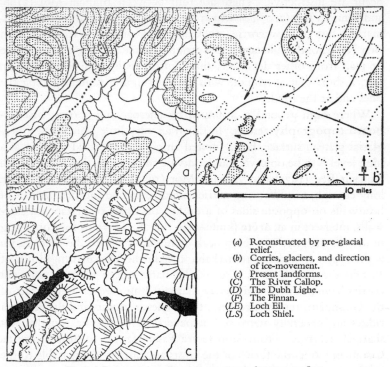

(a) Reconstructed by pre-glacial relief.
(b) Corries, glaciers, and direction of ice-movement.
(c) Present landforms.
(C) The River Callop.
(D) The Dubh Lighe.
(F) The Finnan.
(LE) Loch Eil.
(LS) Loch Shiel.

Fig. 4. Diversion of Drainage by the Agency of Ice
(Based, by permission, on part of Sheet 47 of O.S. Scotland (Popular) 1/63,360)

in the field and unmistakable in perspective along a trough reveal themselves on the map only when very large and especially clear-cut, for example, the eastern flank of Sgor Chalum (1369). The rock-steps which typify many glacial troughs, and which are in part responsible for the irregularities of long-profile, are not always revealed by contours even when the contour interval is small. The major rock-step or "trough's end," near the head, is the most likely to be identifiable, since as a rule it is high and stretches the whole way across the trough (cf., in the valley of Allt Coire an Eoin, the small steps at 221733 and 218729 with the great step running through 210720, which rises as far as 2,250 ft. O.D.). Like many small rock-steps, *roches moutonnées* can scarcely be represented, unless by a special symbol on a large-scale map. There are several noteworthy groups in the area of this map, including a fine series in the Callop valley between 910804 and 925793, of which the map gives no hint. Terminal valley moraines, which are numerous, are again unreflected by the contours. Their small, chaotic mounds cannot be shown on the scale employed, even where the range of height is sufficient. Lateral, medial, and ground moraines are also unrepresented.

Renewed Normal Erosion

Since deglaciation there has not been time for streams to achieve grade in the new normal cycle, and torrential reaches and falls are numerous. The waste-mantle is similarly ungraded, for many slopes remain oversteepened by glacial action and bare of the debris of weathering. Nevertheless the details of relief have already been considerably modified, especially by deposition.

On some upper slopes frost action, together with the rapid removal of loose material, has tended to maintain a freshly denuded aspect, but on the lower slopes and in valley bottoms the forms of glacial erosion may be widely and often also thickly covered. Sheets of rock-waste, in places bare scree and in others with a covering of soil and plants, commonly lie banked against the lower parts of the trough walls. These conditions are excellently displayed on the north-eastern side of lower Glen Nevis, where debris-sheets conceal the true steepness of the rocky sides. Elsewhere the masking waste is moraine rather than scree, as in the Loch Eil valley to the west of Fort William.

The very many streams testify to impermeable rock and a heavy rainfall. Run-off is rapid down the steep hillsides, even allowing for the fact that hill peat acts as a reservoir, with the result that trunk streams are very powerful at times of high water. The short lateral tributaries bring down much rock-waste, which is deposited where they are checked on the floor of the main valley or in a lake. Few of the delta-fans on the land are perceptible on the map, partly because the ground is in any case generally varied in fine detail, but lake deltas on the other hand are distinctly outlined by the plan of the shore. Lateral deltas may nearly approach the fan shape, as at Stronchreggon House (0672), but lake-head deltas are frequently less regular (e.g. at Kinlochetive, 1145). Damming of a lake may cause lateral deltas to be drowned, and lead underwater contours to be omitted from the map, as with the Blackwater reservoir on northing 60.

Most of the rock-waste in sheets of scree, deltas, alluvial flats, and related forms is either re-sorted moraine or the product of weathering, but corrasion by post-glacial streams has also provided some. On the map, the effects of this corrasion are best detected where a rock-step or the lip of a hanging valley has been deeply notched, as at 280734. (Note the sharp re-entrant in the 1,750-ft. and adjacent contours.)

Glacial Troughs and Through-valleys

Soundings in the freshwater lochs of Scotland, as in other ribbon lakes elsewhere, prove great depths. Loch Morar, a freshwater loch adjacent to the west coast of Scotland, descends some 1,000 feet below sea-level. Although detailed investigation is required to show how much of the barrier at the lower end of a lake consists of moraine, and how much rock in place, there can be little doubt that in many glacier troughs erosion was deepest some way above the glacier snout. Towards its lower end, a Pleistocene valley glacier must, like the glaciers of to-day, have been much reduced by melting and ablation, so that its cross-sectional area diminished down-valley. This is one explanation of the "down-at-heel" erosion which excavated the great lake basins. In their original form they must have been even more impressive than they now are, for some have been completely silted up, while in the remainder alluvial infilling has made progress to a varying degree.

Now these enormous hollows cannot have been formed unless the basal ice moved locally up-hill. Such movement is made possible by the very large cross-sectional area of a glacier, by comparison with the cross-sectional area of a river with an equivalent discharge. The comparison is well illustrated at any glacier snout. Because ice-streams are so wide and thick, they can override irregularities in their beds behind which rivers would be impounded. It is necessary to emphasize the phrase *glacier bed*, for the great troughs were the *channels of glaciers*. This fact is usually advanced in explanation of hanging tributary troughs, which are taken as the channels of tributary glaciers. The tributary ice entered the main glacier accordantly, at the surface, but required a much smaller channel—hence the difference of height between the channel floors now revealed by deglaciation.

The explanation thus briefly outlined is acceptable when the hanging tributary leads back into the high ground, and terminates in corries, but some lateral troughs merely pass through a divide into the next trough (cf. that at 2257). As the U-section of these cols testifies to the passage of ice through them, it is evident that at some points ice has spilled over the divide. Accessible examples of the resultant glacially moulded col occur on either side of Dun Deardail (1270), where two small gaps in the crest lead out of Glen Nevis and debouch *above* the corrie at the head of the next valley on the south. It seems certain that ice has passed southwards over the divide here.

Divergence of ice-streams in this manner, made possible by their great thickness, may be associated with local uphill movement towards the lateral outlets. Linton has convincingly demonstrated that, at a number of sites, the sill of the over-ridden col has been much lowered, whether by the lateral over-spill of distributary glaciers—**glacial diffluence**—or by ice-movement across divides—**glacial transfluence.** At some points the rivers, recommencing the work of normal erosion on deglaciation, have flowed through the lowered cols *across* the lines of pre-glacial divides in the direction taken by the diffluent ice. Elsewhere two rivers, flowing in opposite directions in a glacial trough, are separated by a very low watershed. It can often be shown, or at least inferred, that the pre-glacial divide has been destroyed and substituted by an imperceptible or temporary parting, for example that formed by a delta-fan. Two distinct pre-glacial valleys have been merged into a single trough or **through-valley,** so called because it pierces a broad divide or runs through generally high ground from side to side.

Both sets of conditions appear to be represented on this map. At 271643 and 240695, for instance, the parting between opposed drainage in a glacial trough is most ill-defined: ice must have passed along the whole length of the trough, moving away from its gathering-ground and eroding outlet channels. It is unnecessary at the present juncture to comment on the significance of through-valleys in relation to routeways, since the facts are evident enough in themselves and belong, in any event, under another head; but it is well to emphasize that through-valleys, formed in the manner described, are typical of glaciated highlands and to be deliberately looked for in map interpretation.

Diversion of Drainage

The effects of glacial diffluence in river diversion are probably illustrated by the country between Glenfinnan (9080) and Drimsallie

(9578). The Dubh Lighe descends from a tributary trough into the Loch Eil valley, where it turns sharply eastwards. The Callop, descending the opposite side, turns sharply westwards instead of joining the Dubh Lighe, and enters a narrow defile through the high ground. Near their elbow-bends the two streams are separated by a very low divide, scarcely perceptible on the map but seen, in the field, to consist in part of river-laid debris. Since the *roches moutonnées* within the defile (referred to above) present their **stoss** or **onset** sides to the east, it would seem that the gap is due, at least partly, to ice which passed westwards through it. Thus field evidence supports the hypothesis that map interpretation suggests, namely that the Callop flows westwards along a former line of ice-movement, and that its sharp turn is the result of glacial diversion not of river capture in the normal cycle. Although in a full study certain additional facts, for example, strandline movements, would have to be taken into account, the hypothesis as stated is satisfactory as far as it goes. It does provide a possible explanation of the drainage forms, while river capture does not.

Relation of Drainage to Structure

It should now be seen that the problem of the drainage pattern in glaciated highlands must be approached with caution. Even if the Scottish Highlands had not been glaciated, many pitfalls would await the unwary: the drainage net represented on this sheet cannot possibly be interpreted in terms of the stream system of an ideal scarpland—a fact too often overlooked. A little explanation will make the matter clearer. In areas of uniclinal strata, where drainage is to some extent adjusted to structure, streams of any size will flow roughly parallel to the dip or else roughly parallel to the strike, either as a whole or in their various reaches. The abrupt angle where a large stream changes from flowing down-dip to flowing along the strike is most obviously interpreted as an elbow of capture. But in the Scottish Highlands the structural grain is very different from that of a scarpland. Although there is an indescribable variety of detail, it is probably justifiable to say that large areas are dominated by two sets of linear structures which intersect at a high angle. Consequently the broad pattern of relief— of ridges, valleys, and the rivers in them—itself tends to be angular. In the part represented on this map a number of valleys run approximately east-west, while a second group trends from north-east to south-west.[1] The scale of relief makes it clear that the rocks of the

---

[1] The Ben Nevis mass, an old volcanic centre, does not display the same graining.

whole area are resistant. The lines of weakness which the valleys follow are determined by structures not by outcrops. In such country, especially after glaciation, the idea of dismembered consequent streams ceases to be helpful in map interpretation, for angular bends in stream courses are seen as the natural result of adjustment to structure.

Changes of Base-level

The two topics outstanding have in common a relation to former base-levels of erosion. The Parallel Roads in the north-east, symbolized on the map by double pecked lines, are so nearly horizontal as to seem undoubtedly referable to some local series of base-levels, which can scarcely have been provided by anything but bodies of water contained in the valleys. Nothing more can be read from the map; but, as is well known, the Roads are the littoral benches of temporary lakes impounded by ice. Glaciers from the Ben Nevis group blocked Glens Gloy, Roy, and Spean, which filled with meltwater up to the level of the lowest open col. As lower cols were uncovered by the melting ice the lake-levels intermittently fell and benches were cut-and-built at the new shorelines. It may be added that the benches are generally narrow, especially those intermediate ones which are not shown on the map. The controlling spillway at about 850 ft. was a lateral drainage channel, unspectacular but distinctly recognizable on the ground at 288812, at the outlet at the lower end of Glen Spean, where lake-water escaped past the wasting but still obstructive ice which descended from the mountains to the low ground.

Earlier in this chapter it was stated that some of the highest ground, above corrie level, displays subdued relief. Although frost-riving has attacked these elevated sites they do not seem to have been overridden by ice, and might therefore provide some slight indication of the form of the pre-glacial landscape. Within the limits of this map, many summits to the west of Glen More and in the extreme north-east are found to lie within, or very little outside, the range 2,000–3,000 ft. with a majority between 2,000 and 2,500. A wider area would have to be studied before the possible significance of this distribution could be fully appreciated, but one can at least make a note of the relatively small range of height, and advance an extremely tentative suggestion that the numerous summits in the range 2,000–2,500 ft. may be remnants of an erosional surface of low relief. East of Glen More, in the Ben Nevis group and in Mamore Forest, a number of summits rise above 3,000 ft. and some above 4,000. If the possible subdued erosional surface at the lower level is authentic, the higher mountains in the south-east might well have risen above it as monadnocks.

Lowland Glaciation

It is a text-book commonplace to contrast highland glaciation, dominated by erosion, with lowland glaciation, dominated by deposition. The generalization should not be pressed too far, for some lowland parts of the Laurentian and Baltic Shields were centres of ice dispersion, and have in consequence been stripped of their waste-mantle and deeply scoured besides; but the resulting terrain of multitudinous rock knobs, lakes, and watercourses—**mammillated topography**—is poorly represented in Britain, where ice did in fact move outwards from the hills and leave thick deposits on the low ground.

At the farthest limit of advance, where melting held the ice-front stationary, debris accumulated in **terminal moraines;** temporary halts in the decay of the ice-sheet are marked by **recessional moraines.** In front of the moraines, the debris has in many places been redistributed as **outwash** sands and gravels, in some areas pitted by the **kettles** where detached masses of ice were buried and melted. Much of the outwash material was transported by streams of meltwater issuing from the ice-front, often from tunnels within or beneath the glacier. Fans of debris laid down by streams of this kind now appear as roughly conical hills of gravel, called **kames,** while the stream courses themselves may be recorded in gravelly ridges—**eskers**—which wind across country. On **beaded eskers,** kames occur from place to place, marking points at which the ice-front rested for a time.

Examples of all these forms have been located in Britain, but for various reasons are not well shown by the standard map. It will be realized that, comparatively speaking, none is of great size, so that they easily escape representation with a contour interval of 50 ft.—especially as half the contours are interpolated. Again, the English Midlands, where the effects of glacial deposition in a lowland tract could be well displayed, have mostly remained ice-free since the older Pleistocene. Their drifts have been deeply dissected and in part destroyed. Finally, the features mentioned are characterized not only by their form, which a sufficiently detailed topographical map would show, but also by their geological composition. Just as the low sinuous ridge of an esker is concealed on the topographical sheet by a general irregularity of surface, so the material of which it is made is included, on the standard geological map, in a wider spread of glacial drift. Work in the field, and special maps, must provide the illustrations of these smaller features of lowland glaciation.

Drumlins

The greatest sum effect on relief is produced by the sheets of boulder clay, with their associated sands and gravels, which in places thickly conceal the topography of the "solid" rocks. Some boulder-clay spreads cannot be identified from the topographical map, but the interpreter working on lowland parts of the Midlands, on East Anglia, or on the eastern plains should be aware that he is likely to be dealing with a drift cover, more or less complete. Valley trains of outwash, like many river terraces, are also likely to escape notice. In some of the glacially impounded lakes known to have existed on the English Plain great amounts of sands, gravels, and laminated clays were laid down, but neither the lake deposits nor the shoreline features are usually distinguishable on the O.S. map. In contrast to all this lack of information, **drumlin swarms** are unmistakable. As exemplified on the selected 1/25,000 sheet, drumlins consist of low hills of oval or elliptical plan, 50–100 ft. high and $\frac{1}{4}$–$\frac{1}{2}$ mile long. They occur in close-set groups, as here, with their longer axes roughly aligned in a single direction, giving rise to the "basket of eggs" topography. Their exact mode of origin has been keenly argued, but there is little doubt that they have been moulded by a vigorous ice-sheet, principally from ground moraine, but in places from the solid rock. The ice near the ground moved parallel to the long axes of the drumlins—in this tract, along N.W.–S.E. lines in the centre and north, and W.–E. in the south, centre, and east. The actual direction of movement can be found by close study, for drumlins usually taper more gradually at the one end than at the other. The blunter is the **stoss** end, from which the ice came, the sharper is the **lee** end, which points the direction of movement. Unless contours have been carefully surveyed at close intervals it is not always possible to detect on the map a systematic tapering throughout the drumlin field, but the expected asymmetry is suggested by the contours of Ketland (720184), Hemmel Hill (742133), Bermer Hill (743149), and others. The point should be very carefully checked, for the basal ice which moulded the drumlins did not invariably move down-valley. Hollingworth has proved that in the

Eden valley, wherein the mapped area lies, basal ice-sheds did not all coincide with the centres of dispersion on high ground. The drumlins shown on this 1/25,000 sheet were shaped by basal ice which moved south-eastwards from near Appleby and swung eastwards to pass over the higher ground near Stainmore.

Immediately after deglaciation, drumlin fields typically contain many small enclosed hollows, occupied at first by lakes. In suitable climatic conditions these hollows tend to be filled by peat, often in the form of raised bog as in parts of the Irish drumlin country. Here in Edenside the shallow basins have generally been drained, whether naturally by tributaries of the vigorous Eden, or artificially. Note that the pattern of the minor streams is reminiscent, on a small scale, of the theoretical pattern of consequent drainage in an area of Jura-type folding: streams run along the hollows, parallel to the long axes of the hills, passing from one hollow to another by way of the low saddles between adjacent drumlins.

In the south-west, south-east, and north-east, the drift is thin or absent. In the south-west the land is shown to rise above 950 ft. O.D.; the drumlins appear to be confined below the 700-ft. contour. Observe also the deep narrow valley of Waterhouses Beck, which with the quarries marked at several points indicates solid rock. The symbol used for the quarries is that for rock-drawing, not for earth-slopes (cf. 702111, 712128). At the second of these a short spur of railway linking the quarry with the main line indicates that the stone is worth transporting over some distance, which would not be true of boulder clay or ill-assorted gravel. At 701128 a resistant outcrop forms Swathburn Crag. Small quarries in the extreme south-east, served by field roads, seem likely to have provided the building stone for the houses of Winton. In the north-east the valley wall rises sharply for as much as 1,000 feet: it seems to be based on almost horizontally bedded Carboniferous Limestone, for the general assemblage of features is very similar to that found on Ingleborough (see Chapter VII): scars, springs near the foot of the slope, rare and discontinuous streams above, caves (718189), sinks (for example Carry Pot, 770190), abundant scree or more scattered debris (for example Alme Bank, 768186), and possibly also limestone pavement (775188).

The steep edge was obviously in being before the drumlins were formed, for post-glacial re-grading in the normal cycle has not greatly changed the general aspect of the drumlin field and cannot therefore have had much effect on the more resistant "solid" rocks. The physique of the whole area, as interpreted from the 1/2,5000 map, might therefore be summarized in terms such as the following—

A drumlin field, moulded by basal ice moving in a broad arc from north to east, occupies the floor of a wide valley which slopes towards the north-west. The valley is bounded on the north-eastern side by a steep edge, developed across (probably) Carboniferous Limestone, which also underlies at least part of the drumlin field. Karstic features are developed on the limestone to a somewhat limited extent, although it does not seem to have been thickly covered by glacial drift. The drumlin field is in an early stage of dissection by normal drainage; the trunk stream, the Eden, is cutting down rapidly and shows signs of developing a meander-belt, but although any small lakes have been filled in or drained, the tributaries do not seem to have effected much erosion.

NOTES AND REFERENCES

The descriptions of glaciated landscapes given in the texts listed at the end of Chapter II may be amplified from—

R. F. FLINT. *Glacial and Pleistocene Geology.* Wiley, New York, 1957.

The map used to illustrate glaciated highland in the first edition of this book was the old Popular Sheet 47. Because the Lorn and Lochaber Tourist sheet omits part of the area represented on Sheet 47 (Popular), while giving a greater total coverage, little use is made here of the abundant signs of glaciation—including breaches—which occur in the south.

The extent to which field-work modifies and amplifies conclusions drawn from maps alone can be judged by comparing the foregoing interpretation of the Callop breach with—

G. H. DURY. "A Glacial Breach in the Northwestern Highlands," *Scot. Geogr. Mag.,* lxix, 1953, p. 106.

Other accounts of glacial breaching include—

G. H. DURY. "A Contribution to the Geomorphology of Donegal," *Proc. Geol. Assoc.,* lxx, 1959, p. 1.
D. L. LINTON. "Some Scottish River Captures Re-examined." *Scot. Geogr. Mag.,* lxv, 1949, p. 123.
D. L. LINTON. "Some Scottish River Captures Re-examined, II." *Scot. Geogr. Mag.,* lxvii, 1951, p. 31.

D. L. LINTON. *Watershed Breaching by Ice in Scotland.* Institute of British Geographers, Publication No. 15. George Philip, London, 1951, p. 1.

Drift spreads of lowland areas, and certain marginal features, are described in—

S. E. HOLLINGWORTH. "The Glaciation of Western Edenside." *Quart. Journ. Geol. Soc.,* lxxxvii, 1931, p. 281. (Includes a map and discussion of the drumlin field of which part is shown on the selected map.)

C. P. CHATWIN. *East Anglia and Adjoining Areas.* Second Edition. British Regional Geology Series, H.M.S.O., 1948. (See Chapter VI, p. 57 ff.)

V. WILSON. *East Yorkshire and Lincolnshire.* British Regional Geology Series, H.M.S.O., 1948. (See Chapter VIII, p. 71 ff.)

The geology of the country represented on the selected maps is outlined in—

T. EASTWOOD. *Northern England.* Second Edition. British Regional Geology Series, H.M.S.O., 1946.

H. H. READ. *The Grampian Highlands.* Second Edition (Revised by A. G. MacGregor). British Regional Geology Series, H.M.S.O., 1948.

J. PHEMISTER. *Scotland: The Northern Highlands.* Second Edition. British Regional Geology Series, H.M.S.O., 1948.

For an illustrated account of the Parallel Roads of Glen Roy, see *Scotland: The Northern Highlands* (above), p. 74 ff., Fig. 22, Plate IX.

The survival of unglaciated parts amid a generally glaciated highland is discussed by—

D. L. LINTON. "Unglaciated Areas of Scandinavia and Great Britain." *Irish Geography,* ii, 1949, p. 25.

CHAPTER VII

CARBONIFEROUS LIMESTONE COUNTRY

Behold a labyrinth of hydraulic pipes.—BROWNING

MAP: O.S. 1/25,000, SHEET SD/77 (INGLEBOROUGH)

IN tracts underlain by limestone, solution tends to be the most effective agent of erosion. When the limestone is thick, soluble, and well-jointed, but also mechanically strong, systems of cavities are hollowed out which absorb not only the local precipitation but also the largest streams which pass on to the limestone from adjacent impermeable outcrops. The texture of the landscape and the system of drainage come to differ so markedly from those observed where creep, surface wash, and surface streams are at work that limestone country is looked on as evolving in a special cycle, the **karstic cycle.** The name is from the type Karst on the eastern side of the Adriatic.

Recognition of Limestone Country

It is important that a map interpreter should recognize country which is so highly specialized, both as a type of physical landscape and as a form of environment for human life. The most reliable evidence is provided by the sinks whereby drainage passes underground. Surface drainage is discontinuous, intermittent, or absent; dry valleys and enclosed hollows with no surface outlet can also be looked for, together with exposed surfaces of limestone more or less severely weathered. All these are true karstic features, by some or all of which limestone outcrops should be identified on the map. Lime kilns, where they occur and are named, provide useful supporting evidence, especially when quarries adjoin them, but unspecified quarries alone are of little help except in proving resistant rock. Certain additional features are widely observed on the Carboniferous Limestone of this country—lead mines, numerous prehistoric sites, and heathland vegetation—but these are not confined to the limestone and cannot therefore be taken as diagnostic. They should be regarded rather as expected occurrences on limestone outcrops which have been recognized by their physical features.

Sinks

The essential unit of a karst landscape is the **doline**, a conical hollow which may be hundreds of feet across. Comparable and related features in this country may be grouped as **sinks**, a term applicable throughout the range from true dolines to enclosed marshy basins and minute depressions. Many sinks[1] appear to be connected with more or less vertical shafts (the **pitches** of spelaeologists), which develop at the intersection of major joint-planes, and are best displayed where they are kept open by a disappearing stream. In the Chalk country some groups of localized sinks and shafts are known, but the rock appears to be too soft to support and preserve large systems of cavities. It is moreover permeable, and therefore soluble, in mass, so that much rainfall is disposed of by wholesale percolation and dry valleys are more typical than sinks. Karst country proper is well represented in the selected area, which is not based on Chalk, and where the several varieties of sink may be observed on Ingleborough. Hundreds more occur than are shown on the 1/25,000 sheet. Some of the larger hollows are symbolized by hachuring, as, for example, in the kilometre square 7272. A number of deep conical sinks are found here, although the surface drainage is concentrated in nothing more than rills. On the eastern flank of the mountain perennial streams are swallowed, as Fell Beck at Gaping Gill (751727) and Alum Pot Beck at Alum Pot (775756). In the absence of the hachure symbol a well-marked terminal sink may be recorded in a place-name, for example, Hodge Hole (735756), or by a note, for example, "Enters Pot Holes" (759768), "Mouth of Cave" (762730). Sinks of this kind are rarely blocked. The disappearing stream tends to cut through the lip of the shaft, lowering its profile upstream with reference to this local base-level. Thus the valley is deepened as far down as the sink but not below it, while the sink itself is enlarged as the sides are weathered back. The **blind valley** resulting ends in a steep enclosing wall. Other streams dwindle gradually through small openings in their channels, ceasing to flow above ground at a point which varies with the season and which is determined by the combined effect of discharge and the condition of the sinks upstream. Many of the smaller streams mapped here disappear in this manner, so that one cannot with complete certainty interpolate sinks at their lower ends.

---

[1] Sinks are known in various localities as swallows, swallow-holes, swallets, sink-holes, pots, and potholes.

Nevertheless, when marked sinks and probable sinks are plotted (Fig. 5) it is found that a systematic arrangement can be made out. The higher, steep-sided part of Ingleborough discharges surface

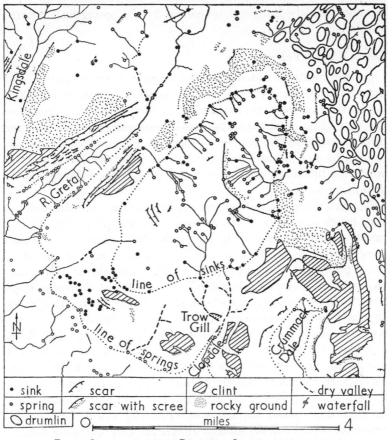

FIG. 5. INTERPRETATION OF PHYSIQUE: INGLEBOROUGH AND ITS
SURROUNDINGS
(Based, by permission, on Sheet SD/77 of the O.S. 1/25,000 Map)

streams, which nearly all vanish at a line of sinks encircling the mountain at a height varying between 1,200 and 1,500 ft. O.D. The stow thus enclosed is one of impermeable rock and the line of sinks approximately marks the upper boundary of the limestone, beyond which the waters circulate underground to reappear at very well-marked lines of springs low down in the valleys. As none remains at the surface, the drainage of the limestone tract is mature in the karstic cycle. In fact, the stage is that of late maturity, for normal erosion is re-asserting itself on the impermeable rock which underlies the limestone and which is being revealed in the valley bottoms. The junction with the limestone is marked by the spring-lines referred to (Fig. 5).

Other Karstic Features

On the limestone outcrop as thus delineated, other features of a karst landscape may be sought. They may be dealt with under two heads: those related to the circulation of underground water, and those due to weathering at the surface. Although the cavern systems and their associated surface features connect the sinks and springs already mentioned, it is more convenient to deal first with the features of weathered limestone, which are well expressed on the map and are well understood.

Between the spring-line and the line of sinks one can make out, in a very rough way, a succession of surface features (Plate IIA). On the steep valley walls above the springs, individual resistant beds of limestone have been thrown into relief by differential erosion, and stand out as precipitous rocky **scars** (Fig. 5). Debris weathered off the scar-face tends to accumulate in a bank of scree lower down the slope. Some of the many sheets of rock-waste are symbolized on the 1/25,000 sheet and on the sketch-map. An interesting modification of the scar-scree association occurs on Keld Bank (7477), below Bent Hill Wood (7777) and elsewhere; although the scar has been weathered back into the hillside and covered with soil and vegetation, a bank of scree survives, running across the slope, to indicate the near-by presence of a strong limestone bed. Scars are naturally best formed and maintained on steep slopes where the debris of weathering can be most quickly removed. On the flatter hilltops above, the bare limestone beds are exposed in limestone pavements, or **clints,** shown on the O.S. map by a variant form of rock-drawing. Clints are fields of joint-blocks, each block separated from its neighbours by **grikes,** the fissures opened by solution along joint-planes. Away from the bounding scarps clints pass into rock-strewn ground with a partial soil cover, distinguished on the O.S. map by the symbol for scattered boulders, and that in turn into expanses of peat moor. The "Moss" names (for example on the south-west flank of Ingleborough) and the various bogs are significant of climate as well as of vegetation type.

Thickness of the Limestone

Now the spring-line shown in Fig. 5 is not far from horizontal. It lies close to 850 ft. in the Greta valley, where the springs are remarkably aligned, ranges vertically through c. 100 ft. in the south-west, and is included between the 900-ft. and 1,000-ft. contours in Crummack Dale in the south-east. One may infer that the base of the limestone is nearly flat and level. The attitude of the scars, which run sub-horizontally across the hillsides, confirms this inference by showing that individual beds of limestone dip very gently. It follows that the vertical distance between the spring-line and the line of sinks may be taken as a rough guide to the total thickness of the limestone. A figure of the order of 500 ft. seems the most reasonable.

Underground Cavities

A limestone formation of this thickness, late mature in the karstic cycle, is bound to include extensive systems of cavities through which water passes from the sinks to the springs; but, on a map, information is usually restricted to the names of a few well-known caves; it is rare for the outlines to be shown, as they are here at Ingleborough Cave (7571). Without such guidance, the interpreter should refrain from explaining certain features by the collapse of caverns, as he may at first be tempted to do. The need for this caution arises from the occurrence in a karst landscape of enclosed hollows, not only the small sink and the larger doline, but in addition the **uvala** and the **polje.** The polje, unknown in this country,[1] may be 100 square miles or more in area and is of tectonic origin. The uvala (or valley sink) is a basin of intermediate size, formed by the merging of two or more dolines. The feature is not common in Britain, but is not unknown. Now the underground cavity systems include three elements: the joint-plane cave previously mentioned, the gallery (passage, or, in gently-dipping strata, bedding-plane cave), and the large cavern or hall which is long, wide, and deep. There must be a limiting size, above which the roof of a cavity can no longer support its own weight. Collapse of large bedding-plane caves would cause shallow depressions at the surface, like the subsidence-hollows of coalfields; the unroofing of halls would produce uvalas and gorges; more localized collapse at a shaft might be reflected in a deep doline. Investigations show, however, that the upper parts of cave systems tend to become choked

[1] Unless possibly at Lane End, Bucks.

by detritus and stalagmite, rather than to be enlarged still more by solution, flaking, and corrasion. Hence in map interpretation, gorges and enclosed hollows should be noted merely in descriptive terms. Trow Gill (7571) on the present sheet (see also Fig. 5) is known to have been cut, at least in part, by a surface stream which flowed during the Pleistocene. Similarly, the common dry valleys of a karst may have large sinks in the bottom, as has that between Gaping Gill and Trow Gill, but it cannot be assumed that the former surface stream follows its old line with the sole difference of flowing at a lower level and underground. The dry limestone valleys of Britain should be regarded generally as carved by surface streams, which have been captured to the underground system, and which as a result may find an outlet in entirely separate valleys at some distance away. The dry valley symbols in Fig. 5 must therefore *not* be taken as suggesting underground courses: they merely show features which on the 1/25,000 sheet are expressed by contours.

A number of the springs at the base of the limestone are likely to fluctuate greatly in volume, in response to local rainfall, siphoning, and flow under pressure, but unless the map gives descriptive notes the interpreter can do little more than remark the issue of considerable streams, for example, at Clapham Beck Head (754711).

Rocks Above and Below the Limestone

Limestone formations in Britain, of the order of thickness estimated here and with pronounced karstic features developed on them, may be confidently regarded as Carboniferous Limestone. Of the underlying impermeable rocks little can be said, except that they are older than Carboniferous. The name "Ingleton Granite Quarries" (7175) is misleading, including a quarryman's term, not a geologist's. Above the Carboniferous Limestone in the higher part of Ingleborough are younger strata, for the most part impermeable since there are many surface streams, but including some permeable beds to account for the occasional sinks. It is likely that the permeable rocks too are limestone, and that they explain the few scars in addition to the well-defined springs.

Evidence of Glaciation

In the north-east of the area mapped is part of a drumlin field. The discussion of Chapter VI need not be amplified here: it is necessary only to note that the arrangement of many drumlins indicates a southward movement of ground ice down the Ribble valley. Sinks in the grid squares 7974 and 7975 prove that the drift cover is in places thin. Apart from the drumlins, the map affords no indisputable evidence of glaciation. The straightness and trough-like form of Kingsdale and the Greta valley might well be structurally determined rather than glacially shaped. One cannot judge how widely the hill peat is developed on boulder clay which, as it were, waterproofs the limestone. The fact is that the whole area has been powerfully glaciated, but does not lend itself readily to the development and preservation of glacial landforms. In the field the most striking evidence consists in the numerous erratic boulders of grit scattered over the clints: they are unrepresented on the map.

River Development

On a map of this size and scale, the area represented (less than forty square miles) is too small to afford the wide synoptic view required in the interpretation of drainage and drainage history. Because of this limitation, and because the landscape is complicated by karstic, glacial, and structural features, certain important results of normal erosion are obscured. The series of falls on the Greta, like the **force** on Jenkin Beck (7173), are in reality located at knickpoints, the headward limits of waves of rejuvenation. Another probable knick belonging to an earlier cycle occurs on the Greta at Weathercote (7377). It has been shown by Sweeting that the great mountain shoulders at c. 1,300 ft. O.D. are to be regarded as erosional rather than structural: the close coincidence of an erosional platform and a structural surface is mainly accidental. None of these facts can be perceived on the map: they are mentioned here as a reminder that interpretation, however careful and detailed, is subject to inevitable limitations by comparison with work on the ground.

NOTES AND REFERENCES

For a general account of the geology, see—

D. A. WRAY. *The Pennines and Adjacent Areas.* Second Edition. British Regional Geology Series, H.M.S.O., 1948.

The concept of the karstic cycle is briefly summarized in—

E. M. SANDERS. "The Cycle of Erosion in a Karst Region (after Cvijic)." *Geogr. Review,* xi, 1921, p. 593.

An illuminating morphological study of the whole district in which Ingleborough occurs is—

M. M. SWEETING. "Erosion Cycles and Limestone Caverns in the Ingleborough District." *Geogr. Journ.*, cxv, 1950, p. 63.

Other relevant material is to be found in—

R. G. S. HUDSON *et al.* "The Geology of the Yorkshire Dales." *Proc. Geol. Assoc.*, xliv, 1933, p. 227. (I: "The Scenery and Geology of North-west Yorkshire," by R. G. S. HUDSON; III: "Alum Pot," by H. W. HAYWOOD; IV: "The Glacial and Post-glacial periods in West Yorkshire," by A. RAISTRICK.)

A very detailed study of Ingleborough was published under the name of T. McKENNY HUGHES in *Proc. Yorks. Geol. Soc.* "Physical Geography" appeared in 1901, "Geology" in 1905–8 inclusive.

Current research and exploration, illustrated by detailed maps, are described in the periodicals *Cave Science* and *Transactions of the Cave Research Group*.

Papers describing the modifications of karstic phenomena observed in the Chalk country are listed at the end of Chapter IV.

CHAPTER VIII

COASTS AND SHORELINES

What's it now?
Changed like a rock-flat, rough with rusty weed,
At first wash-over o' the returning wave.—BROWNING

MAPS: O.S. 1/63,360 (SEVENTH SERIES) SHEETS 114 (BOSTON
AND SKEGNESS), 186 (BODMIN AND LAUNCESTON); O.S.
TOURIST MAP, 1/63,360 (LORN AND LOCHABER); O.S.
IRELAND, 1/63,360, SHEET 169, ETC. (WEXFORD); O.S.
1/25,000, SHEETS NC/76 (SUTHERLAND), SY/18 (SIDMOUTH)

THE concept of a cycle of erosion is no less useful in the study of
shorelines than in the study of landscapes. Youth, maturity, and old
age are marked by distinctive assemblages of forms. In some ways
maps of shorelines are easier to interpret than those of inland areas,
for many shoreline features are very simple to represent on a map, and
the principal changes in the course of the shoreline cycle are changes of
plan. Moreover, shorelines become more and more regular as maturity
approaches, whereas landscapes become progressively diversified.
On the other hand, while it is often unnecessary or impossible to
consider the effect on inland areas of changes of base-level, whatever
they may have been, evidence of such changes is critical in the interpretation of shorelines. Away from the coast, the essential fact is that
the land lies above base-level and is subject to subaerial processes; at
the shore, neither the direction nor the amount of strand-line movements can be ignored.

The Shoreline Cycle

Any considerable displacement of the strand-line initiates a new
cycle of shoreline erosion on the drowned landscape or the exposed
sea floor. Hence the customary distinction between **shorelines of
submergence** and **shorelines of emergence.** A third class, **neutral
shorelines,** includes the shorelines of deltas, volcanoes, and fault-
blocks, where neither submergence nor emergence is required to
account for the initial forms. In nature, **compound shorelines** are

widespread. They combine elements essential to any two, or all three, of the foregoing classes. Shorelines with both emergent and submergent features are especially common.

It must be understood that the terms "submergence" and "emergence" mean nothing more than movements of the strandline, upwards—**positive,** and downwards—**negative,** respectively. Nothing is implied as to causes. Examples of local or regional uplift, depression, or tilting, are well known from certain unstable parts of the earth's crust, but there is also powerful support for the view that world-wide rises and falls of sea-level have taken place. These general or **eustatic** movements of the strand-line appear to have been going on at least since early Pliocene times. Some must be due to changes in the capacity of the ocean basins, but others reflect the loss or gain of water resulting from the growth or decay of the great Pleistocene ice-sheets. It is easy to see that, quite apart from crustal deformation, the record of strand-line movements on a given stretch of coast may be lengthy and involved. Hence the wide distribution of compound shore-lines, and the need to employ non-committal descriptive terms in speaking of changes in base-level.

Besides the direction and extent of the strand-line movement with which the new shoreline cycle begins, it is necessary also to consider

Type of Strand-line Movement	INITIAL RELIEF	
	Highland	Lowland
NEGATIVE— Emergence	Emergent highland shoreline	Emergent lowland shoreline
POSITIVE— Submergence	Submergent highland shoreline	Submergent lowland shoreline

the form of the emergent or submergent land. As far as the stage of maturity, the shore-line cycle takes a different course on highland and lowland coasts respectively. Some accounts over-simplify matters by assuming or implying that emergent and lowland coasts on the one side, and submergent and highland coasts on the other, are synonymous. This is frequently, but not universally, true. A eustatic rise of sea-level must obviously submerge lowland as well as highland, while in places the bottom topography is far too rugged to constitute a lowland if it emerged. Consequently the initial shorelines produced by strand-line movements must be cross-classified in the manner illustrated in the table on p. 68.

Compound shorelines combining emergent and submergent features may be appropriately described in such terms as "compound highland shoreline, dominantly submergent."

The Shoreline and Subaerial Cycles

Now a map interpreter will rarely confine his attention to the shoreline—the immediate zone of contact between land and water—but will need to treat the coast as a whole. In this connection the direction of strand-line movement is more than ever important, for a rise of base-level influences the development of rivers and valleys differently from a fall. In this wider view, it is necessary to pay attention not only to raised shoreline features, including perhaps extensive wave-cut platforms, but also the breaks of river profile and to valley-in-valley forms; but, although a given strand-line movement may be looked on as initiating a new cycle both on land and at the shore, it is usually convenient to consider the landscape and shoreline individually, for several reasons. Even if the two cycles begin simultaneously, it does not follow that they will keep in phase after the initial stage. Furthermore, the intermittent movements of emergence abundantly proved in many areas have been relatively small and frequent, initiating epicycles rather than completely new cycles of subaerial erosion. Consequently a landscape and its limiting shoreline are commonly found to be in very different stages of their respective cycles, a fact which must be recognized in description. The physical characteristics of a given piece of coast may be summarized under the following heads—

1. Class of shoreline—submergent, emergent, neutral, or compound.
2. Type of coast—highland or lowland.
3. Stage reached in the shoreline cycle.
4. Form of subaerial cycle—normal, karstic, glacial, or arid—and stage reached therein.

The areas discussed below can be no more than a selection of the combinations possible. They are, however, intended to illustrate a wide variety of coastal forms, and to exemplify the main features developed in the shoreline cycle up to and including the stage of maturity, with particular reference to highland coasts in different stages of the subaerial cycle.

HIGHLAND COAST WITH FEATURES OF EMERGENCE. EARLY YOUTH OF THE SHORELINE CYCLE. LANDSCAPE YOUTHFUL IN THE NORMAL CYCLE AFTER DEGLACIATION
O.S. 1/25,000, SHEET NC/76

This portion of the coast of Sutherland displays a remarkable combination of features. Although no submarine contours are given, the amplitude of subaerial relief and the forms produced on the shore indicate that the highland variety of the shoreline cycle is in progress. Numerous lakes on the low plateau seem most likely to be the relics of glaciation, which has also left its mark in the steep-sided flat-bottomed trough glimpsed in the extreme south-west. It is not surprising, therefore, to discover signs of re-grading in the new, post-glacial, normal cycle, as at 738622, 783620, and 785629, where streams are sawing through rock-steps or through the lips of hanging valleys. Some additional factor may be needed to explain the well-marked gorge in the east (798630), to which another in the south-east may be tributary, but without more evidence this problem cannot be explored.

One soon finds, however, that not all active valley-deepening can be explained as the re-grading of glacial features. Several tiny valleys hang notably above the shore, discharging their streams in cascades down the cliff. At 752658 and 753659 the "hang" is more than 100 ft. At some points the stream, in commencing to accommodate itself to present base-level, has deeply notched the cliff-face, for instance at 774655; but inspection of the contours proves that the work is still in its early stage and that the long-profile still plunges seaward. A number of these ungraded streams appear too long to have developed headwards from the present shore: they are something more than rills. Consequently an explanation must be found for the steep gradients near their mouths. The leading possibilities are cliff recession and rejuvenation by emergence. To cause a stream to hang or plunge in this way, cliff recession must be rapid and extensive. But, as will shortly be noted, the forms of this shoreline indicate very early youth and resistant rocks, whence it may be inferred that in the present shoreline cycle the cliffs have receded very little. The alternative explanation, late emergence, is amply supported by the available evidence.

At the head of Armadale Bay (7964) a low cliff is marked (in hachuring) above HWMOST, backed by a gentle ascent up to 100 ft. or thereabouts, after which there is a sharp rise. Near Kirktomy (74638) a flat spur rises a little over 100 ft. O.D., and closed 100-ft. contours occur at 735635 and 708625 in neighbouring valleys. The steep rising slopes behind Farr Bay (7162) commence at about the same level of 100 ft. One may suggest—subject to the test of work on the ground—that the features noticed are the remains of former cliffs and abrasion-platforms, mostly referable to a base-level of c. 100 ft. above the present one. If so, the low cliff in Armadale Bay appears to record a still-stand at an intermediate level during emergence. Since heavy glaciation would have been likely to destroy or to conceal evidence of this kind, the inferred high base-levels are probably later than local deglaciation.

These features of relatively late emergence of a highland coast are associated with the shoreline forms of very early youth. The shoreline as a whole is **crenulate,** i.e. minutely irregular. Besides the bold irregularities of bay and headland there are very many small clefts and points, etched out by wave-erosion working selectively along lines of weakness. At this stage the details of shoreline form are to a considerable extent structure-guided, as is well shown in the group of parallel clefts just east of Port Mor (7363). As yet bay-head beaches are little developed: powerful waves enter nearly every inlet and maintain steep cliffs along most of the shoreline.

SUBMERGENT COAST OF SUBDUED RELIEF. HIGHLAND
SHORELINE, APPROACHING SUB-MATURITY. LANDSCAPE
POST-MATURE
O.S. IRELAND, 1/63,360, SHEET 169 (SHEETS 169, 170, 180, 181)
(WEXFORD)

Submergence is likely to produce **embayed shorelines.** Within this group a very wide range of initial forms is possible. In schematic outlines of the shoreline cycle on a submergent highland coast, it is as a rule tacitly assumed that the landscape is approximately mature in the subaerial cycle, so that the former valleys constitute deep bays while the intervening divides stand out prominently in headlands.

In these circumstances, wave-attack on the promontories gives rise to cliffs. The derived rock-waste combines with the load discharged by rivers to provide material which is disposed as beaches, spits, and bars. The chief process at work in cliff-cutting, in rolling and abrading the beach material, and in moving it along the shore, is wave-action. Despite the multitude of individual forms, both destructional and constructional, one may observe a general tendency for beaches to accumulate at the heads of bays and for headlands to be linked to one another by coalescent spits. By the time the shoreline is sub-mature, much of the headlands has been destroyed; the surviving bays are almost cut off from the open sea by bars, which with the headland beaches form a straight or gently curving, regular line. Maturity is attained when the line of beach has been pushed back to the mainland throughout its whole length, i.e. when the cliff line has receded as far as the bayheads.

Although the selected area is not one of very strong relief, the shoreline cycle is that appropriate to highland coasts. Submergence is indicated by the drowned valleys: Bannow Bay and Wexford Harbour are identical in kind with Tacumshin Lake and Lady's Island Lake. Perhaps it is not out of place to insist that, although the outlines of bays are smoothed out by shoreline processes, the actual inlets are usually the mark of submergence. In other words, most of the excavation has been done by subaerial not marine agents. The fact that a bay coincides with an outcrop of weak rock does not prove that the inlet has been carved out by the sea. Observation shows that shoreline processes tend to regularize, not to diversify, the outline. Initially this particular shoreline must have been deeply embayed, but a great deal of regularization has already taken place and sub-maturity has been reached in places. The different stretches may be taken one by one, in order of advancement in the shoreline cycle.

Bannow Bay seems to have been a fairly deep, steep-sided valley, cut by a river working to a lower base-level than the present. Submergence must have converted it into a deep-water inlet of the **ria** type, with a bottom gradient determined by the form of the old valley floor. Doubtless the bay originally deepened seaward, but the old floor now lies deeply buried under rock-waste that has accumulated since the submergence, filling the inlet up to mid-tide level and replacing deep water by tidal flats. It is often urged that tidal scour militates against the silting-up of inlets of this kind, but tides can sweep material in as well as out. Observation teaches that these inlets usually tend to become choked, and the limited investigations so far made show that much of the fill consists of marine rather than fluvial deposits. In some measure the silt is protected by the bar typically developed across the mouth of the inlet. There is a difference between the offshore bar, formed under water and driven landward, and the spit which grows out from a headland. Here the channel on the western side of Bannow Island is about two-thirds closed by a large spit projecting north-eastwards from the opposite shore; a mile to the southward, the bar at the head of Fethard Bay almost completely encloses a small drowned valley.

Between Crossfarnoge and Carnsore Point the cycle is more advanced. No powerful streams enter the sea; baymouth bars almost seal off the two inlets. The forms are those of sub-maturity—a smooth line of beach passing from one cliffed headland to another, with portions of the initial inlets surviving.. Note that spits appear to have grown most vigorously from the central headland, which is now **winged,** both to east and west—a fact which should prevent any facile generalization on the dominant direction of longshore drift. Although it may be possible to show that, on a long stretch of shoreline, there is a net transport of beach material in a single direction, local exceptions are to be expected if the shoreline is at all irregular (cf. the opposed directions of the spits in Bannow and Fethard Bays).

The shoreline of Ballyteige Bay is not far from mature. It may be assumed that the headlands on either side, now well cliffed, once projected farther, and that they have receded considerably under wave-attack. The great dune-covered bar (Ballyteige Burrows) is the counterpart of the baymouth bars previously noticed, but has been driven inland as the anchoring headlands were destroyed until it rests almost against the mainland. The sizeable bay of submergence behind it is now represented by no more than a narrow valley bottom with diminutive tidal flats. A further recession of less than a mile would involve the burial of these flats, the destruction of the bar, and the development of a smooth line of cliffs on the firm ground. This stretch of shoreline would then be fully mature.

It seems as if the large bar has grown westwards from Crossfarnoge, progressively displacing the mouth of the stream. Where records exist, however, it is remarked that such growth and displacement have usually been intermittent and subject to relapse, even without human interference. The map can give no more than a statement of existing conditions, showing effective growth and ignoring historical details, unless a given spit or bar is obviously complex or compound. **Complex spits** are those which send out branches during growth; **compound spits** include elements of more than one earlier feature; **recurved (hooked) spits,** for instance, not infrequently have "teeth" on the landward side, at former positions of the terminal hook. On the present map the record is somewhat obscured by dunes, which incidentally prove that the spits are at least partly composed of sand, and by sea walls at the edges of the tidal flats. The long spit terminating in Rosslare Point is possibly compound, but the irregular inner edge may also be due to tidal deltas (washovers), where beach material has been swilled inwards at high tide. Small spits which would be more easily understood with the help of bottom contours are St. Patrick's Bridge near Crossfarnoge, St. Patrick's Bridge on Saltee Island Little, and The Ring on Saltee Island Great.

The eastern shoreline remains to be considered in its entirety. The low cliffs alternating with shallow bays between Carnsore and Greenore Points call for little remark. About a mile beyond Rosslare Harbour Pier a smoothly curved shoreline begins, based in the south on the mainland but farther north on the spit already mentioned. It is clear that the shoreline is being developed to some extent independently of the subaerial forms, a fact which emphasizes the utility of dealing separately with the shoreline and with the landscape. The spit, already protecting a great width of tidal flat from wave-attack, seems likely to unite with The Raven to the north in a cuspate bar, separating Wexford Harbour from the open sea. On this view, the shoreline from Rosslare Harbour northwards is roughly sub-mature, but if it were a lowland shoreline the interpretation would be different (see below, p. 77 ff).

HIGHLAND COAST. SHORELINE MATURE IN THE PRESENT
CYCLE. LANDSCAPE YOUTHFUL
O.S. 1/25,000, SHEET SY/18 (SIDMOUTH)

This part of the shoreline of South Devon is in reality compound. The River Sid has a buried channel related to a lower base-level, while raised abrasion-platforms in the vicinity show where the sea formerly stood higher against the land; but maturity in the present shoreline cycle is so nearly attained that for the purposes of this discussion strand-line movements may be ignored, the shoreline being regarded as one of submergence, exemplifying a later stage in evolution than that just discussed.

There are no bays. Any headlands that may formerly have existed have been cut back to a smooth line of cliffs, broken only at the valley mouths and continuously fringed by beach (Plate IIB). Such regularity, and the abrupt truncation of the landscape are typical of shoreline maturity. There is no doubt that neither geological structure nor the texture of the subaerial relief has much effect on the plan of the shore, nor do waves enter and enlarge the openings of river valleys.

The area seems to be one of uniclinal structure, with a more resistant cap-rock overlying weaker beds. Note at the top of each valley wall a steep descent through about a hundred feet, with a gentler slope below.[1] Wave-attack is vigorous and the cliffs are receding rapidly. Small streams hang above the shore, or plunge downward to their mouths, having been unable to lower their profiles as fast as the cliffs have been cut back. The discordant relationship of minor drainage to present base-level is similar to that observed previously on the Sutherland shoreline, but the cause is different. In Sutherland other evidence supported the hypothesis of emergence; here, rapid and general retreat of the cliffs is indicated not merely by the mature form of the shore, but also by the partial destruction of hilltop camps at High Peak Hill (104859) and Berry Cliff (188882). It seems probable that marine erosion has made a great deal of progress in the last two thousand years or so. The whole cliff-face, not the lower part alone, is being brought down. Landslip symbols, particularly clear on Berry Cliff, show how the weak rocks respond to undercutting.

HIGHLAND COAST, DOMINANTLY EMERGENT BUT ALSO SHOWING FEATURES OF LATE SUBMERGENCE. COMPOUND SHORELINE, YOUTHFUL IN THE PRESENT CYCLE. POLYCYCLIC LANDSCAPE, YOUTHFUL IN THE PRESENT CYCLE
O.S. 1/63,360 (SEVENTH SERIES) SHEET 186
(BODMIN AND LAUNCESTON)

The maps so far treated in this chapter represent many of the larger features typical of submergent highland coasts, at various stages up to and including maturity of the shoreline cycle. Stress has been laid on

---

[1] This inference is correct as far as it goes, but a geological map would reveal additional facts of great interest: the cap-rock rests unconformably on the weak formation; the flat summit-surface, although apparently structural at first sight, truncates the resistant beds at a very low angle, and is thought to be a plane of marine abrasion.

shoreline rather than on subaerial forms. It is now proposed to take a more complicated example, where an upland in early youth of the subaerial cycle has been affected by oscillations of the strand-line, including a late positive movement, and where the present shoreline is still immature.

The initial shoreline of submergence was very different from that of a submerged mature landscape. Instead of the ample bays, corresponding to wide and deep valleys, one observes long, narrow, branching inlets: this is a ria coast. The partially submerged valleys of the Fowey, Looe, and Lynher, comparable to Barrow Bay in County Wexford, are indisputable criteria of submergence. Wave-erosion cannot have shaped them. They inherit their form from the young valleys of the subaerial cycle in progress before submergence. As expected in a youthful landscape, the narrow valleys are separated by broad divides, on whose flat tops part of the initial surface survives. These divides end seaward in rather irregular lines of steep cliff, which correspond to the cliffed noses of the headlands which result from the drowning of a mature landscape.

Additional evidence of a rise in base-level is given by the submerged forest (2150) whose trees must have flourished above the sea-level of the time. It is possible also that the floor of St. Austell Bay is a drowned bayhead beach; but the drowned valleys remain the most easily interpreted sign of submergence, even in the field, as shoreline features developed at lower levels than the present are necessarily under water. Evidence of emergence, in contrast, is often unmistakable on the ground: caves, arches, stacks, wave-cut notches, patches of abrasion-platform and of raised beach may be located, all out of reach of the highest waves.

On the map, however, such comparatively small features do not show well, if at all, and are rarely labelled. Hence emergence has to be proved from inland areas. It is unnecessary to recapitulate the arguments of Chapter V, where it was seen that in this area strongly rejuvenated drainage is associated with a series of probable erosional platforms, the whole indicating intermittent falls of base-level. The interpreter would do well to note that except for the presumptive evidence of a former low base-level afforded by the rias, shoreline forms as represented on maps are best able to indicate submergence. Away from the shore, however, emergence may be clearly recorded in the erosional forms of valleys while submergence is concealed by an alluvial fill which may not be apparent from the topographical sheet.

The shorelines mapped here are by no means mature in the present cycle, but the work of regularization has begun. Bayhead beach is slightly developed in Mevagissey and St. Austell Bays, while the rias are being filled in; the mouth of the Seaton River (3054) is indeed already choked by alluvium behind a small enclosing spit. It seems likely that the shoreline will attain a smooth plan long before the cliff line has been cut back to the heads of the rias; the inlets will disappear mainly by being silted up, until the tidal flats are replaced by flood-plain, i.e. until shoreline forms are locally replaced by subaerial forms. The shoreline cycle is most advanced in the south-east. East of Downend Point (2251) cliff recession from a shelving shore has left an abrasion-platform, which passes eastwards in Whitesands Bay into a gently arcuate beach. The line of cliff on this stretch is approaching the regular plan of maturity.

LOWLAND COAST. COMPOUND SHORELINE, DOMINANTLY
SUBMERGENT, IMMATURE
O.S. 1/63,360 (SEVENTH SERIES) SHEET 114
(BOSTON AND SKEGNESS)

The initial outline of a lowland coast is likely to be highly irregular or generally smooth, according to whether the cycle begins with the submergence of a land-surface or with the emergence of a flat sea-floor. As strand-line movements at various times in the late Pliocene, the Pleistocene, and the post-Pleistocene have been widely demon-strated in Britain, it is probable that most immature lowland shorelines will be compound. It is best to remain content with the fact that the lowland shoreline cycle is in progress, and to ascertain the stage reached with present base-level.

Whether emergent or submergent, the lowland shore has a bottom gradient so gentle that large waves break offshore. In doing so they throw up a bar, submarine at first, but appearing above water at the end of the initial stage. The bar grows by accretion as more debris is thrown up, but at the same time time tends to move inshore as the seaward face is combed down and fresh material is washed over the top towards the mainland. During the stage of youth, the lagoon enclosed between the bar and the mainland becomes filled with rock waste and organic debris—silt and peat—over which the bar is driven inwards. Maturity is reached when the bar has been pushed back to the mainland, which is itself attacked. Conditions at this stage are generally similar to those at maturity of the highland shoreline cycle, except that on the mature lowland shore the cliffs can be of no great height.

It is of course possible for the gentle bottom gradient required for evolution of the lowland-shore type to exist locally off a highland coast, for example, where slight emergence brought the floor of a bay within reach of the breaking waves. For this reason care is necessary in interpreting such features as those of Wexford Harbour, where the shoreline is known to be compound. On the present map, however, the very wide tidal flats in the Wash leave no doubt that the lowland shoreline cycle is being pursued.

In Britain generally, lowland shores have been greatly modified by reclamation and drainage. The flat fenlands here, and the comparable Somerset Levels, represent former lagoon and marsh. The remarkably wide bar, easily distinguished from the fen by its contrasted pattern of settlement and roads, is the compound product of several strand-line movements, which cannot however be inferred from the map. This shoreline will not be mature until the bar has receded across the fen, to rest against the firm ground which commences near the 50-ft. contour. One may doubt whether recession is taking place at the present time, for south of Gibraltar Point (5557) a strip of salt marsh has been reclaimed on the seaward flank of the bar (see also Chapter XII), and the work is still going on. North of the Point conditions are different. A much narrower foreshore corresponds to a steeper bottom gradient. No salt marsh was available for reclamation here, for the shoreline runs along the edge of a sandy bar which is, in places at least, under wave-attack. There is nothing to say whether the "-ness" of Skegness was an earlier tip of the bar, but one may certainly note the apparent southward diversion of the Steeping River (5460–5567) and of the drainage now carried in the artificial Cow Bank Drain (5560). The groynes near Chapel St. Leonards indicate a longshore movement of beach material as well as the likelihood of marine erosion, while the outlines of Chapel Point and Ingoldmells Point suggest that the movement is towards the south. It seems justifiable to infer that the seaward face of the bar tends to be combed down, and that the material transported along the beach accumulates at the tip of Gibraltar Point, extending it southwards.

In spite of the redistribution of material on the outer side, great bars of this kind appear to be, as features, fairly stable. Inshore movement is slow, often perhaps because of artificial defensive works. Some offshore bars of shingle, or banks of sand and mud, are relatively fast-moving, changing noticeably in their low-tide outlines between successive surveys. It is very difficult to generalize about their development. In map interpretation it is advisable merely to note them as indications of shallow water and of the form of shoreline cycle to be expected.

FIORD COAST
O.S. TOURIST MAP, 1/63,360 (LORN AND LOCHABER)

Fiords are glacier troughs invaded by the sea. They are frequently compared to the rias of some unglaciated areas, presumably because they indent the shoreline and allow the sea to penetrate deeply inland, but the comparison needs to be qualified. Rias necessarily imply submergence, fiords do not. Rias are river valleys, excavated when base-level was lower and drowned by a positive strand-line movement: fiords are glacier channels, occupied by the sea when the ice melted. Because of their great size glaciers can corrade well below sea-level. Now as many ria coasts are thought to have remained stable—unaffected by earth-movement—since late Tertiary times, the submergence which has affected them would seem to have been eustatic, the manifestation of a general change of base-level. Some heavily glaciated areas, on the other hand, responded to the massive load of Pleistocene ice-caps by regional subsidence from which they are still intermittently recovering. Movements of this kind, due to loading or unloading, are termed **isostatic.** It will readily be appreciated that, although submergence is not an essential factor in the origin of fiords, many fiord coasts bear the impress of positive movements as well as displaying the more noticeable signs of emergence. Hence in addition to noting those features which derive from glaciation, or from the beginnings of re-grading in the normal cycle, one must pay close attention to the shoreline in the attempt to discover evidence of recent changes in base-level.

In many glacier troughs the "solid" rock is deeply buried under moraine and alluvium, which conceal irregularities in the floor; but in ribbon lakes and fiords deposition is concentrated at the mouths of rivers, with the result that enclosed hollows survive to be recorded in the underwater contours. On the Scottish O.S. sheets bottom contours, given in feet for all freshwater lochs except where the level has been raised by damming, clearly indicate the forms present. In that part of Loch Shiel mapped on Sheet 47 there are three closed contours at depths of 400, 400, and 300 ft. Similar subsidiary basins occur in Lochs Arkaig and Lochy in the north, and in Loch Eilde Mor in the south-east. Some of these hollows reflect the presence of rock-steps, but each basin as a whole owes much of its depth to the "down-at-heel" erosion characteristic of valley glaciers. In the fiords submarine contours, drawn at 5 and 10 fathoms only, can often record no more than the shallowing towards the lower end: in Loch Eil both are closed; in upper Loch Linnhe both converge at, but pass through, the Corran Narrows (0263); the floor of Loch Leven is better represented, with the 10-fathom line closed at least four times and with two sets of narrows less than 5 fathoms deep.

Just as the sides of a glaciated trough plunge below an alluvial fill or beneath the surface of a ribbon lake, so they descend sharply into the waters of a fiord. Hanging tributary valleys and deltas at the fiord heads or at the mouths of lateral tributaries bear the same relationship to the main trough as do comparable features inland, which have already been reviewed. It is not to be expected that in the sheltered waters of fiords marine erosion will have advanced far since deglaciation, so that wave-cut cliffs are unlikely to be extensive. The influence of communication with the sea is found in the features of occupance (discussed elsewhere) and in the beaches.

All these sea-lochs are fringed between tide-marks by a narrow strip of foreshore, very narrow where the bottom plunges but wider where the larger deltas provide gentle gradients. In the freshwater basins, beach development, if any, is small. Above the present sea beaches, close examination of the fiord shorelines discloses a narrow bench at a slightly higher level (Plate IB). Where it is best developed this feature might well be interpreted at first sight as a delta flat, an accumulation of moraine, or as the enclosing rock at the lower end of a glacier trough. The small flat at North Ballachulish (0560), with a spot height of 46 ft., could be based on the rocky or morainic barrier of lower Loch Leven; the low ground projecting eastward at the Corran Narrows might be similarly related to the basin of upper Loch Linnhe; the narrows at the lower end of Loch Eil seem to combine the terminal shallowing of a glacier trough with the delta of a heavily laden tributary. At other points, however, explanations of this kind cannot apply. Opposite Fort William at Trislaig (0974) a small flat appears between the edge of the water and the line of buildings. The fiord appears to be deep hereabouts, and receives no delta-building stream.

Much of the ground up to 50 ft. is obscured by the road symbol, but hints of comparable sites appear north of the Klachnish delta (0669) and along the southern shore of Loch Eil. Indeed, the course of the coast roads, and of the railway on the north of Loch Eil, itself suggests that low ground is available. On the south side of Loch Leven the 50-ft. contour runs along the water's edge, indicating a continuous slope, and the main road climbs the valley wall. Elsewhere careful inspection discovers that the 50-ft. and zero contours are more widely separated than those above. In fact, the coast roads skirting the water's edge run along raised beach, except when crossing streams and deltas, or passing over rocky knobs.

The interpretation is not easy on this map scale, but a careful interpreter might expect to locate the flat at Trislaig and to consider it in relation to possible isostatic movement. Much of the rest follows. Account may also be taken of spot-heights on the coast roads, but caution is necessary here. Those on bridges and deltas should be rejected as likely to be misleading. The whole series, in order along the coast road from 9359 to the head of L. Eil is: 15, 52, 41, 24, 38, 45, 31, 12, 27, 15, 45, 21, 40, 27, 15, 11, 12, 30, 19, 10 ft. Some of these would certainly be eliminated in the field, as marking crests where the road crosses a protuberance, but in map interpretation they must be taken as they stand. It would be straining the evidence to claim that they are helpful: in twenty-five readings there is a range of 35 ft. and little sign of grouping. The sample is too small to suggest what is actually the case, that more than one raised beach exists as a result of intermittent isostatic recovery. Again, the map scale is too small and the contour interval too large to show what is at once noted in the field, that rejuvenated streams have partly destroyed their raised deltas, building anew at the lower level. The resulting "cone-in-cone" form is well displayed on the ground at the northern side of the Loch Eil narrows.

It is thus seen that the topographical map is not wholly successful in representing on this fiord coast certain features which, although small in extent, throw much light on recent shoreline evolution and considerably modify the setting of human activity.

NOTES AND REFERENCES

For general accounts of geology, see—

J. PHEMISTER. *The Northern Highlands.* Second Edition. British Regional Geology Series, H.M.S.O., 1948.

V. WILSON. *East Yorkshire and Lincolnshire*. British Regional Geology Series, H.M.S.O., 1948.

C. P. CHATWIN. *East Anglia and Adjoining Areas*. Second Edition. British Regional Geology Series, H.M.S.O., 1948.

G. A. KELLAWAY and F. B. A. WELCH. *The Bristol and Gloucester District*. Second Edition. British Regional Geology Series, H.M.S.O., 1948.

H. DEWEY. *South-west England*. Second Edition. British Regional Geology Series, H.M.S.O., 1948.

A full treatment of shorelines is—

D. W. JOHNSON. *Shore Processes and Shoreline Development*. Wiley, New York, 1919.

Much helpful material may be obtained from—

J. A. STEERS. *The Coastline of England and Wales*. University Press, Cambridge, 1946. (In particular, wave-action, longshore drift, and spits are discussed on pp. 44–63, and strand-line movements in Chapter XII, pp. 475–501. Some of the stretches of coast treated in the foregoing text are considered on pp. 198–204, 211–12, 254–60, 420–438.)

The account of constructional forms given in this chapter might usefully be supplemented by STEERS, *op. cit.*, pp. 345–64 and by—

J. L. DAVIES. "Wave Refraction and the Evolution of Shoreline Curves," *Geographical Studies*, v, 2, 1958, p. 1.

C. A. M. KING. "The Relationship between Wave Incidence, etc.," *Trans. Inst. Brit. Geog.*, 1953, p. 13.

Papers relating to the shorelines described in the foregoing chapter include—

J. F. N. GREEN. "The High Platforms of East Devon." *Proc. Geol. Assoc.*, xlii, 1941, p. 36.

O. D. KENDALL. "The Coast of Somerset." *Proceedings of the Bristol Naturalists' Society*, viii, 1936, p. 186.

H. GODWIN. "Studies in the Post-glacial History of British Vegetation, III and IV." *Phil. Trans. Roy. Soc.*, B, 230, 1940, p. 239.

H. GODWIN. "Correlations in the Somerset Levels." *New Phytologist*, xl, 1941, p. 108. (See also STEERS, *op. cit.*, pp. 490–1, Figs. 105, 106.)

CHAPTER IX

LANDSCAPE IN AN ARID CLIMATE

The wind
Shoulders the pillared dust.—BROWNING

MAP: DEPARTMENT OF THE INTERIOR, U.S. GEOLOGICAL
SURVEY, 1/62,500 (PINAL COUNTY (ARIZONA) CASA GRANDE
QUADRANGLE)

AN arid climate is one in which potential evaporation exceeds precipitation. It follows that deserts are regions of interior drainage, except where very large rivers succeed in crossing them without drying up on the way; but, paradoxically enough, it is impossible to understand much of the desert landscape without allowing a major role to running and percolating water. Few areas are entirely without rain: rain in the desert, when it does come, takes the form of violent convectional downpours which, running off as heavily loaded torrents or sheets of water, profoundly modify the relief.

Distinctive Character of Desert Landscapes

Landscapes shaped by desert weathering and erosion differ among themselves as signally as do the glaciated landscapes of Britain. Just as in glaciated country, however, the landforms produced are highly characteristic and easily recognizable, whether in the field or on the map. The nature of the geographical environment is never in doubt, and a descriptive account presents few problems. The difficulties are of another kind. As yet, the precise ways in which erosion operates in arid conditions are not fully understood, nor has the scheme of the desert cycle been satisfactorily worked out beyond the stage of maturity. It seems best, therefore, to take the selected map as exemplifying certain leading features of a single class of desert landscape, rather than a particular stage in the desert cycle, and to direct the reader to the works listed below for a discussion of the morphological problems involved, and for descriptions of contrasted arid tracts.

This map represents an assemblage of **inselberg, pediment,** and **alluvial plain.** These are major landforms, sufficient proof in

83

themselves that the processes of arid erosion have been at work. On the ground one would observe an abundant variety of detail, for, as on shorelines, bare rock is exposed to differential attack; but in both cases limitations of scale compel the map interpreter to concentrate chiefly on the texture of relief as a whole.

Inselbergs

The inselbergs are the Sacaton Mountains in the north-east, and a similar mass in the south-west lying mostly outside the Quadrangle and represented only by Double Peaks and near-by smaller hills. Inselbergs are residual forms, rising abruptly—here, to as much as 700 ft.—above the surrounding gentler slopes. Some are based on outcrops of particularly resistant igneous rock, and may be compared to the tors found in humid regions; others are outliers of a partly denuded formation, analogous to the outliers in front of escarpments in the normal landscape. Whatever their composition, inselbergs undergo severe weathering. The powerful sun by day, and unimpeded radiation by night cause great changes of temperature in the exposed rock-faces, which tend to disintegrate into angular slabs or coarse grains. When water is available, heat promotes chemical change. By these means, and with the aid of the natural sand-blast, rock can be speedily worn away. Since the vegetation cover is necessarily sparse and discontinuous, desert landscapes are made up of clear-cut features with associated large accumulations of debris.

Alluvial Plain

It might be thought that the scree would remain banked up against the inselbergs until it was sufficiently comminuted to be removed by the wind. This might be so in completely rainless climates, but is demonstrably not the fact in the Casa Grande neighbourhood. Loose rock-waste has been carried away from the inselbergs, leaving them continually exposed to further attack, and has been transported towards the lowest ground, where it has accumulated in a constructional plain with very low surface-gradients. On this map sheet the constructional surface, nicely defined by widely spaced contours, is approximately bounded by the railway on the north-east and by the upper part of the Santa Rosa Wash on the south-west. The deposits beneath the plain are certain to be generally permeable, and in suitable climatic conditions may contain accessible reserves of ground-water (cf. the numerous wells, especially towards the east).

It is clear that the supply of fine-grained waste is limited. Patches of bare sand, as marked on the map, are mostly small, and dunes are restricted in extent. Moreover, drainage channels occur, even though the streams which flow in them are intermittent, and part of the plain has been settled—impossible conditions in a sand sea. One might reasonably infer, therefore, that the rock-waste on which the plain is based is partly coarse in calibre. It can scarcely have been transported to its present position by wind.

Pediments

Between the eroded inselbergs and the depositional plain lie the pediments, gently sloping surfaces cut across the solid rock and usually covered with the thinnest veneer of rock-waste. The pediment surrounding the Sacaton Mountains lies between the 1,500-ft. and 1,275-ft. contours on the western side, and between 1,600 and 1,400 on the east, while that below Double Peaks is observed to fall as low as 1,325 ft. towards the north. Inselbergs are separated from pediments by a remarkably clear break of slope, below which the pediment surfaces descend smoothly towards the plain at gradients decreasing slightly downwards. Their lower boundaries, where the flat plain begins, are scarcely less well defined although the change of gradient is much less.

The mode of origin of pediments is far too controversial to be debated at length here. Some authorities regard them as planed off by the lateral corrasion of intermittent streams, which work over the pediments much as the streams of humid regions work over deltas, repeatedly dividing and swinging from side to side. In support of this view it is urged that many pediments (including, as is at once noted, those mapped here) are very shallowly dissected by numerous tiny channels. It has been suggested that occasional streams, fed by the rare convectional rainstorms, are capable of transporting the heavy loads of rock-waste derived from the hills, but not of cutting deeply down. On this view, the streams can corrade in the hill belt, just succeed in transporting their load across the pediments, and aggrade the alluvial plain where they disappear by evaporation and percolation. Other writers regard sheet-flood as the chief process at work—the movement of occasional floodwater, heavily charged with the tools of corrasion, over the whole pediment at once. Others again maintain that a pediment is produced essentially by the bodily retreat, under the attack of desert erosion, of the rock-wall above, and would compare it to the strike vales in front of scarps in humid regions. Whatever the truth of the matter, it is generally agreed that pediments are progressively extended as the higher ground is denuded. The useful term **pediplanation** connotes the sum of the processes at work and their total effect. The selected map is seen, then, to depict a tract where pediplanation is going on. The inselbergs now observed are certain to be destroyed. Final stages in their elimination are represented by knobs of rock, isolated or in groups, such as the hill at 1,556 ft. about two miles north-west of Casa Grande, or the detached remnants south of the Sacaton Mountains.

Intermittent Drainage

All the streams of this tract are intermittent. Fed by surface run-off, they cut gullies in the high ground and occupy shifting, braided courses on the alluvial plain, where they lose most of their volume before passing the bounds of the Quadrangle. It is evident that the floor of this particular basin of centripetal drainage rises well above the 1,000-ft. contour.

Desert Basins

This consideration enables the interpreter to regard the landforms identified in due perspective against a wider background of desert erosion in general; for deserts are commonly enclosed by mountain walls, constituting orographic as well as drainage basins. Hence the considerable elevations of floor and walls alike. The encircling mountains serve to accentuate an aridity, which might be expected because of distance from the sea or the prevalence of high atmospheric pressure. Many of the desert basins in the south-western United States are, in fact, the tectonic depressions of highly faulted country, and are bounded by fault-blocks. As the basin walls retreat before the attack of pediplanation, detached portions survive for a time as inselbergs, while the products of weathering accumulate—except for a fraction exported as wind-blown sand—in the hollows. Plain, pediments, rock knobs, inselbergs, basin walls, and the channels of intermittent drainage thus make up a unitary assemblage of forms. The pattern of drainage, the form of slopes, depositional features, and features of erosion are not only characteristic in themselves, but are combined in a distinctive manner. The resulting assemblage is not least instructive in virtue of proving the qualities of the climate in which it has evolved.

NOTES AND REFERENCES

Accounts of landscape development in arid and semi-arid climates may be found in the texts listed at the end of Chapter II. The following should be consulted for a fuller treatment of the problems involved—

R. A. BAGNOLD. *The Physics of Blown Sand and Desert Dunes.* Methuen, London, 1941.

C. A. COTTON. *Climatic Accidents in Landscape Making.* Whitcombe & Tombs, London, 1947.

L. C. KING. *South African Scenery.* Oliver and Boyd, London and Edinburgh, 1951.

Selected papers dealing with the nature and formation of pediments are—

W. G. V. BALCHIN and N. PYE. "Piedmont Profiles in the Arid Cycle," *Proc. Geol. Assoc.*, lxvi, 1956, p. 167.

W. M. DAVIS. "Rock Floors in Arid and in Humid Climates." *Journ. Geology*, xxxviii, 1930, pp. 1, 136.

D. W. JOHNSON. "Rock Planes of Arid Regions." *Geogr. Review*, 1932, p. 656.

J. L. RICH. "Origin and Evolution of Rock-fans and Pediments." *Bull. Geol. Soc., Amer.*, xlci, 1935, p. 999.

CHAPTER X

A COMPLEX LANDSCAPE BASED ON COMPLEX STRUCTURE

*When we come to subdivide areas in detail, to examine the actual differentiation of the earth's surface, the first of our considerations is generally its morphological diversity.—*S. W. WOOLDRIDGE

MAP: O.S. 1/63,360 (SEVENTH SERIES) SHEET 165 (WESTON-SUPER-MARE)

THE constituent stows of this piece of country contrast very markedly with one another, in respect of geological structure, lithology, soil property, form of relief, system of drainage, settlement pattern, and surface utilization; but, although a remarkable variety of country is thus to be observed within a small compass, the task of physical interpretation is not unduly difficult, especially in the light of the foregoing studies. All the kinds of landform present here have already been encountered. This map may therefore be treated in a somewhat summary fashion, stow by stow, in accordance with the morphological analysis sketched in Fig. 6. The subdivision made is based on the principles recommended by Linton[1] and summarized in Chapter II. Each boundary, as may be seen by comparing Fig. 6 and the O.S. map, is drawn along a marked break of slope between two very different types of country. The nature of the differences, that is to say the rational basis of the subdivision, will be made clear in the following descriptions.

1 and 2: Hill Country of the South-west

These stows are undergoing dissection by many short streams, which in the extreme south-west are deeply incised in narrow valleys. Here the land rises to more than 900 ft. O.D. and the rocks appear to be especially resistant. Note also the considerable extent of woodland and moor. The lower ground, on the other hand, has been largely

---

[1] D. L. LINTON. "The Delimitation of Morphological Regions." Published in *London Essays In Geography*, edited by L. DUDLEY STAMP and S. W. WOOLDRIDGE. Longmans, Green, London, 1951.

cleared: wide shallow valleys separate belts of low hills and the under-lying rocks are evidently of no more than moderate strength.

3. The Levels

This is fen country, closely similar in many ways to the fenland bordering the Wash. Much of the drainage is artificial, and the trace of many natural streams has been lost. Note the extremely low altitudes *above mean sea-level* that are recorded far inland. The tidal range in the Bristol Channel is very great, as suggested by the wide tidal flats and the long tidal reach of the River Parrett: hence an increased need of land-drainage works, of embankments along the rivers, and of strengthened coast defences. The strongest defence of the fen is however a natural one. This is a lowland coast, on which bars have been anchored by headlands and islands, with fen deposits accumulating in the former lagoon behind.

The "islands" rising from the fen are of two kinds. The sizable but very low-lying dry patches, only slightly higher than the rest of the Levels, are based on permeable deposits, as suggested by the absence of streams and ditches and the presence of nucleated settlement and roads (cf. the sites of Chedzoy, Middlezoy, and Weston Zoyland (3437 to 3733)). "Islands" of the second kind belong under the next heading.

4. Small Cuestas and Outliers amid the Levels

The Polden Hills constitute a small cuesta, based on rock which is not wholly impermeable. The scarp, which faces S.S.W., is in part marked by strips of woodland. In the neighbourhood of Wedmore (4347) a generally similar block of hills slopes gently towards the south-west and has a steep scarp-face on the north-eastern side. If the two stows are based on a single geological formation, they are to be interpreted as the flanks of a denuded syncline with its axis roughly along the line of the River Brue. Contrast the denuded anticlines studied in Chapter IV, where the scarps were observed to face inwards. Now as Brent Knoll, Glastonbury Tor, and Pennard Hill lie somewhere near the supposed synclinal axis, it may be supposed that they are outliers of a formation younger than that in the Polden Hills and at Wedmore. A synclinal structure is compatible with the fact that they are scarped on all sides. Note also that Glastonbury Tor and Brent Knoll both display a tabular flat c. 300 ft. below the summit. It seems likely that a resistant cap-rock is underlain by weaker beds, and those again by strong rocks which crop out in structural benches. Similar features were noted, and a similar inference drawn, in the study of outliers from the Cotswolds (p. 23).

The hills around High Ham (4231) in the south resemble the south-eastern part of the Polden Hills very closely. If the central syncline were followed on the south-west by a complementary anticline, one might expect a cuesta similar to the Poldens but facing in the opposite direction; but, since the highest and best-formed scarp in these southernmost hills faces north-westwards, at right angles to the front of the Poldens, it is clear that some structural complication has supervened, i.e. that the fold system is not composed of simple, parallel elements.

5. The Mendips and Other Similar Limestone Hills

The Mendips rise abruptly above the valley flats of the Axe on the south and the gentle slopes of the Yeo valley bottom on the north, to a wide, flat plateau surface lying mostly between 850 and 900 ft. O.D. (Plate IIIA). As surface drainage is almost entirely lacking the underlying rock must be highly permeable, and also mechanically strong, for dry valleys become gorges at the edge of the upland with precipitous, rocky walls. These features, together with the caves and caverns noted on the map—a mere selection of the total known—are those of karst country, which one may suppose to be developed on Carboniferous Limestone (cf. Chapter VII).

Although sinks are not marked by a special symbol, the streams flowing northwards off Blackdown (Fig. 6) evidently vanish into the limestone. In actuality, sinks occur at many points but are not shown on the map: one might expect them to be excluded at this scale. The limited development of steep rocky slopes and the apparent lack of limestone pavement are more difficult to account for, but like the paucity of dry valleys are to be related to the remarkably perfect planation of the plateau surface.

One soon realizes that the Mendip plateau is an erosional not a structural surface; for the valley of the Lox Yeo, hemmed in by the western hills, cannot be other than a denuded dome or basin. In other words, the structures in the limestone block are far from uniclinal, not to mention horizontal. The plateau surface is developed across, and regardless of, high and inconstant dips. Brief consideration shows that the Lox Yeo valley has been carved from a short pitching anticline or elongated dome, with the longer axis running approximately east-west. If the structure were synclinal, the impermeable rocks which now floor the centre should be traceable some way to the east by means of a visible stream system. There is, in fact, only a small

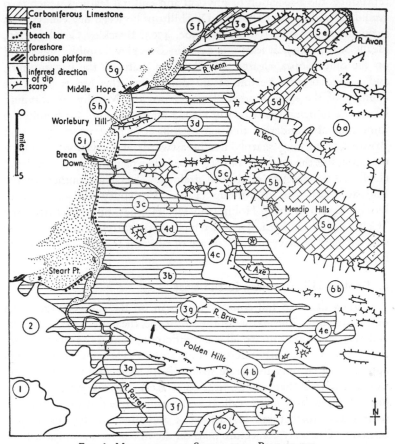

FIG. 6. MORPHOLOGICAL SUBDIVISION: PART OF THE
SOMERSET PLAIN
See text for explanation of numbers
(Based, by permission, on Sheet 165 of the O.S. New Popular 1/63,360 Map)

impermeable outcrop on the high ground of Black Down, which supports the short streams already noted as disappearing underground on the north, into the overlying permeable beds.[1] The small enclosed

[1] The dome was first excavated at least as early as Triassic times, as the 1/63,360 geological sheet proves at a glance, but the topographical map records only the net effect of all erosion and infilling.

lowland is therefore taken as an anticline with its weak core eroded away.

North of the Yeo valley, the western extremity of a group of hills reproduces the association of physical and cultural features which is so well displayed by the Mendips. Dry hilltops between dry valleys with steep and rocky sides (Goblin Combe, 4765, Brockley Combe, 4766, Healls Scars, 4966), at least one cave (in Brockley Combe), woodland on the outer slopes, cleared woodland or heath on the flat summits, and a long barrow permit of no doubt that this too is limestone country of the same kind, differing from the Mendips in standing lower and in being less regularly planed off by erosion. Carboniferous Limestone also underlies the belt of hills stretching westwards from Bristol and turning sharply north-eastwards at Clevedon to follow the coast, but the evidence of rock type is less plentiful here, consisting chiefly in the absence of surface drainage. Detached outliers of the Limestone are seen in Middle Hope, Worlebury Hill, and Brean Down, as also in Steep Holme and Flat Holme; but, apart from the "Celtic Fields" on Brean Down, which might correspond to limestone soil, the only positive indications are of resistant rock of indeterminate type.

6. Broken Hill Country in the East

Heavily dissected hill country comes in on the east, on both sides of the Mendips. The texture of the landscape, the pattern of occupance, and surface utilization are all very different from those observed on the outcrops of Carboniferous Limestone. The underlying rocks appear to be of only moderate strength, for dissection is considerably more advanced than in the limestone areas just reviewed. Broken lines of scarp, and many valleys containing surface streams, indicate sedimentary formations, in part weak and impermeable but in part resistant. One may conjecture that, on the northern side at least, these formations are younger than the Carboniferous Limestone; for the latter, in the outcrop north of the Yeo, forms scarps which face south and west, and should therefore possess an easterly dip which would carry it under the hill belt to the south of Bristol.

The Drainage System

Although rivers of the levels (or the large artificial channels by which they are now represented) are aligned roughly parallel to the grain of relief, they cannot be described as adjusted to structure, for they are not in contact with the solid formations. They flow, instead, over fen deposits which insulate them from the deformed rocks beneath. These rivers should, therefore, be regarded as occupying the infilled valleys of a former landscape wherein the form of the ground was related to structure, and where some measure of drainage adjustment had been attained.

Since little can be discovered of the geological structure of the south-western hills, no comment can be made on the relation of drainage to it, but one may note as a fact that streams here flow in roughly parallel courses towards the north-east. In the Mendips and other outcrops of Carboniferous Limestone the question of adjustment does not arise in the same way. It is more relevant to observe that the drainage may be taken as mature, having gone completely underground.

The map represents an area just large enough to bring out the discordant relationship of drainage to structure in the north-east, where the Avon turns north-westward from a broad valley to pierce a belt of limestone hills in a gorge c. 250 ft. deep. There would seem to be an easier route on weaker rocks, already picked out by the diminutive Land Yeo, through the gap at Flax Bourton (5169). Since the Avon must have become established in its course across the limestone before this gap was eroded, the gorge is seen to be the result of superimposition, which has not yet been followed by readjustment of drainage to the structures now revealed.

The Shoreline

Submergence is proved by the Submarine Forest (2246), while emergence is strongly suggested by the wide expanse of fen behind beach bars, and strikingly demonstrated in the field, for example, by raised beaches north-west of Clevedon: the shoreline is therefore compound. It is dominantly, however, a lowland shoreline of emergence, far from mature in the present cycle, and diversified by headlands where tongues or outliers of resistant rock run down to the sea.

A low offshore gradient and a great tidal range combine to produce a wide foreshore, sandy, at least in part. Dunes have been formed north of the Brue estuary. Wave-built features occur both at and off the shore (cf. the banks such as Langford Grounds off the mouths of the Yeo and Kenn, and the shingle ridge which runs from Stolford (2346) to Steart Point (2847), where it recurves).

At a few places, retreating cliffs cut in resistant outcrops have left a visible abrasion-platform, nowhere widely developed in the northeast but, finely shown in the extreme south-west, where it is $\frac{1}{2}$ mile wide.

NOTES AND REFERENCES

For a general account of the geology, see—

G. A. KELLAWAY and F. B. A. WELCH. *The Bristol and Gloucester District*. Second Edition. British Regional Geology Series, H.M.S.O., 1948.

Special aspects of landform are discussed in—

H. E. BALCH. *The Caves of Mendip*. Fold Press, London, 1926.

A. E. TRUEMAN. "Erosion Levels in the Bristol District, etc." *Proc. Bristol Naturalists' Society*, viii, 1938, p. 402.

H. GODWIN. "Correlations in the Somerset Levels." *New Phytologist*, xl, 1941, p. 108.

The form and distribution of settlement, which are not dealt with in the preceding text, are analysed and described by—

B. M. SWAINSON. "Rural Settlement in Somerset." *Geography*, xx, 1935, p. 113.

B. M. SWAINSON. "Dispersion and Agglomeration of Rural Settlement in Somerset." *Geography*, xxix, 1944, p. 1.

PART II

THE FEATURES OF OCCUPANCE

CHAPTER XI

FEATURES OF OCCUPANCE: GENERAL

And beware how in making the portraiture thou breakest the pattern.—FRANCIS BACON

MAN'S activities have not greatly altered the form of the ground, except locally, where quarrying or tipping has been extensive; but reclamation, drainage, clearing, cultivation, and building have signally altered the observed landscape. To the extent that it fails to portray the visible scene, the map fails to show how little the present countryside resembles the "natural" countryside of prehistory. Forests, woodlands, heaths and marshes of the British lowlands, and of some parts of the highlands, have been replaced by a patchwork of fields, interlaced by man-made roads and thickly studded by settlements. Even the high moorlands, which still remain largely open, have been greatly changed: their treelessness is due in part to the grazing of domestic animals, or to climatic changes which have occurred since the arrival of man.

The study of cultural features lends itself well to map analysis, in the conventional sense of that term—the abstraction from a given map of a certain class of data, such as roads, settlements, or mines. Selective maps produced in this way have an undoubted value in representing, with all possible clarity, distributions which may be somewhat obscured on the full topographic sheet. The interpreter might well make a full analysis of a chosen map at an early stage in his work, taking off the several distributions in turn, in order to demonstrate to himself the wealth of data available and the way in which patterns emerge when various elements are separately studied. The ultimate aim, however, must be to take a synthetic, not an analytic, view—to interpret the map as it stands, and to perceive relationships which are necessarily suppressed or minimized when distributions are taken singly.

Interpretation of Land Use

On the O.S. topographical maps, evidence of agriculture is mostly of a negative kind. With few exceptions, the most highly productive agricultural land is left blank. The existence of a special series of Land Utilization maps is, in itself, a measure of the deficiency. A little thought will show that most of the features of contemporary occupance recorded on the standard maps fall into the category of Waste, i.e. agriculturally unproductive land, in the classification of the Land Utilization Survey. Six other categories are distinguished in that scheme. Two, Inland Water and Forest (which includes all wooded land), are marked by special symbols on the topographical map, so that the interpreter is left in no doubt of their extent and distribution. On the Land Utilization maps, Gardens include nurseries and orchards in addition to domestic kitchen or flower gardens; topographical maps record only orchards by a special symbol, except where the name "nursery" occurs or where, on the 1/25,000 and larger scales, tiny enclosures attached to dwellings are presumably for the most part cultivated. The distribution of heath and moorland, as shown by the familiar tuft symbol on the topographical sheet, is broadly similar to the extent of Heath (land suitable for rough grazing) recorded by the Land Utilization Survey for upland areas, but in the lowlands the topographical maps are liable to omit much, while Arable and Meadow (permanent pasture), accounting for the greater part of the best agricultural land, are not symbolized at all. All the interpreter can do, therefore, in dealing with the map of an area which has little wood, moor, heath, or marsh, and which carries a rural population, is to assume that most of the land is devoted to agriculture.

Needless to say, any specific points of relevant information should be discovered and made use of. The nature of the boundary between enclosed and improved land on the one side, and open, unimproved land on the other, is particularly interesting. Since field boundaries are given on the 1/25,000 series, the extent of enclosure can be found; but, as there is no positive evidence of the quality of the worked land, one must rely on such data as the symbols for limestone pavement or for rocky ground to show which fields are likely to be in pasture rather than in tillage. In areas of crofting settlement, even this evidence is likely to be misleading. Where woodland or heath is widespread in a low-lying tract, the map may also provide inferential evidence of an outcrop of sand or clay, but the possibly more favourable soils of adjacent cleared areas can only be guessed at—not, as a rule, very accurately —by the absence of heath or wood.

Sometimes the beginner, encouraged by having identified the underlying structures and types of rock, is tempted to suggest an agricultural response. Such a practice would be determinism of the crudest sort. It leads directly into a number of pitfalls. Soil type is not determined solely, or necessarily at all, by solid geology. The initial work of the new Soil Survey reveals, as any rational geographer must have foreseen, a most complex and minutely diversified distribution of soil series. Again, land use is not influenced by soil alone. Quite apart from the influence of superficial deposits, of vegetation, of climate, and of cultivation on the qualities of farmland, one must always remember that agricultural distributions are in part a function of historical and economic factors. The Land Utilization maps, drawn from a field-by-field survey in the nineteen-thirties, have already been relegated to the status of historical documents by the agricultural changes which accompanied and followed the war of 1939-45. Bearing in mind that there have been other periods in which no less marked alteration in the structure of farming occurred, the map interpreter must content himself with concluding that a cleared, settled rural area is presumably devoted to agriculture, and with observing the probable extent and limits of cultivation. Within the bounds of worked land, positive evidence is likely to exist in the form of named farms, symbolized orchards and glasshouses, the channels of water meadows, and, in places, such establishments as sugarbeet factories, which by their nature indicate one of the crops raised; but all these, even in the most favourable areas, provide no more than a small fraction of the total possible information.

Routes

Railways and canals, which are features of industrialism, present few problems of interpretation, except that on some map series a more detailed classification might be conveniently employed. Their modes of development, their functions, and their varying success are good general guides. Natural waterways and road systems, however, are more difficult to deal with, partly because their use dates from very early times.

Canals. Canals are usually closely adapted to the form of the ground, running along valley bottoms or parallel to the contours on a slope. The existence of a canal implies that at the time of construction a demand for transport facilities existed, or was expected to arise, but in this country canal traffic has so greatly declined that parts of the canal system now lie derelict. Where canals appear on the map they should be examined for notation (*disused*), which is by no means uncommon.

Apparent signs of present use may be unreliable. Some factories alongside canals are themselves derelict; others prefer road or rail transport, even for the bulky goods which canals are designed to carry. Canal names are worth particular attention: the original purpose of the "Coal Canals" is self-evident, while "Navigation Canals" were often intended as a substitute waterway for rivers on which, for some reason, navigation was difficult. Many canals take off from rivers at points determined by physical obstacles of some kind, but the map evidence is not always clear. One may assume that below the canal junction a river is navigable for canal-boats, as weirs and locks may show. Nothing can be said of larger craft, however, unless the map represents port facilities, for example, coal staithes. It is significant of the small use made of inland waterways in this country that the scale of map symbols makes no distinction on the basis of capacity. Coastal ports are better treated: large harbour works can be shown in plan, while the upstream limit of tides is recorded, on the 1/63,360 (Seventh Series) Series, by a change from the black line of HWM to the blue of inland water.

Railways. The railway network in Britain, laid down piecemeal by competing companies, shows unnecessary duplication of routes in some parts and deficiencies in others. A number of sizeable towns, for example, lie off the main lines. These anomalies apart, railways connect the great towns and industrial districts with one another and with the ports, as well as providing transport services of varying quality in rural areas. Map interpretation is usually concerned with a small part of the system at one time. Consequently, through-connections must be taken for granted, and attention confined to the class of installation shown, the relation of routes to the form of the ground, and the apparent effect of rail services on the location and growth of settlement.

The scale of symbols used for railways varies with the map series, the editions of a single series, and even with the style of a single edition. Thus on the Provisional Edition of the O.S. 1/63,360 (New Popular) maps, railways with two or more tracks are marked by a solid black line, whereas on the later New Popular Edition proper a chequered line is used, similar to that on the 1/25,000 (Later Style). Single-track lines are recorded on both series by a lighter chequer. The distinction between the two classes corresponds to a useful division in railway practice, between lines where two-way working is or is not possible without by-passing. Other track symbols demand careful

Photograph: Aerofilms, Ltd.

(A) Aerial View of the Mouth of the Fowey River,
Showing Low Plateau Inland

Photograph: Aerofilms, Ltd.

(B) Ben Nevis (Centre Distance) Rising above Surrounding
Mountains

Note cultivation on raised beach, left foreground

Plate I

Geological Survey photograph, reproduced by permission of the Controller, H.M.S.O.

(A) GENERAL VIEW OF INGLEBOROUGH AND SIMON FELL

Clints in the foreground

Geological Survey Photograph, reproduced by permission of the Controller, H.M.S.O.

(B) THE SHORELINE NEAR SIDMOUTH

The band of beach can be seen to cross the mouth of the River Sid at the extreme
right. Abrasion-platform in the foreground

PLATE II

reference to the key of the map: a hatched line on the 1/63,360 O.S. sheets means a siding or tramway, but on the 1/25,000 scale stands for a narrow gauge railway; sidings on the 1/25,000 appear as solid black lines. For narrow gauge tracks the Seventh Series 1/63,360 uses an adaptation of the chequer symbol. The 1/25,000 indicates clearly which factories have rail connections; the 1/63,360, on close examination, will reveal the location of marshalling yards, goods yards, and railway depots.

Railways are less closely adapted to relief than are canals, partly because sharp bends in the track are impracticable and because a certain gradient is permissible. Nevertheless, where relief is at all varied one usually finds that the actual course of a railway line is a compromise between the straight line from point to point and the line of least gradient. Conversely, a long straight track is a guarantee of very low natural gradients, but with this exception each stretch must be discussed on its merits in respect of guidance by relief features.

In examining the relation between railways and the growth of settlements, one must recall that in long-settled countries most villages and many towns already existed as villages and towns, before the railways were laid. Consequently, railways as a factor in locating settlement need little attention, but they can be shown, on the other hand, to have influenced the manner and rate of expansion of pre-existing settlements. The remarkable growth of towns in occidental countries, which began in the nineteenth century and has continued into the twentieth, cannot be looked on as *caused by* the construction of railways: urbanization and railways alike are the outcome of that complex of developments, the Industrial Revolution; but, since, for the purposes of industry, large quantities of goods and large numbers of people must be transported from place to place, it is natural to look for some connection between the spread of towns and the existence of a rail link.

The connection is most obviously revealed where a town has grown towards, and across, a railway. When the lines were first laid they usually skirted the towns then in being, so that where they now run through a town it is often found that they have been included by recent growth. Sometimes the early stage of the process is illustrated, as where a town has not yet spread beyond the tracks, or where the original nucleus of settlement lies at some distance and a newer group of dwellings has been established near the station. Many of the clearest examples of the stimulating effect of a rail connection on the rate of growth, and on the direction of growth, are to be found in dormitory areas, where small towns or villages are within easy reach, by rail, of a large industrial town. Swollen dormitory villages along the railway correspond to ribbons of housing along main roads, where motor transport is the stimulating factor.

Roads. The pattern of roads is essentially composite. It has had a far lengthier evolution than have the networks of canal and rail, and combines antique elements with those of very recent origin. In the broadest sense and as a whole, it is the most intimately associated with the pattern of settlement. Furthermore, although canal and rail have exercised their effects on the distribution of factories and on the direction of urban growth, roads are now recovering their dominance. The most recent industrialization, generally post-1920 and by no means at an end, demands vast facilities for road transport of goods. Travel by road has increased no less remarkably. It is not surprising that in Britain the road system, alone of the three networks, still tends to grow. The additions include new arterial roads and by-passes as well as new streets in expanding towns.

Completely new roads, however, are rare, for changing needs have been met by widening and re-surfacing rather than by entirely new construction. The great road-makers of the later eighteenth and early nineteenth centuries also achieved a compromise between improvement and substitution. Only under the Romans was a single planned system imposed on the whole country. Many elements of that system can be distinguished in the present road network, but even where the Roman line is preserved it may be followed in part by bridle tracks and footpaths instead of by metalled roads. The dismemberment of the Roman roads clearly illustrates the manner in which the present system, symbolized on the map according to present condition and function, results from long-continued growth, selection, adaptation, superimposition, and abandonment.

In map interpretation, therefore, the classification of roads should be looked on as a rough guide to present use. A better general view of the whole system is obtained when all roads, of whatever grade, are traced off the map and indicated by a uniform symbol, when unsuspected through-routes are likely to appear. Frequently the relation of the road system to the forms of the ground will also be more clearly seen, for the various elements of the modern system are, as it were, re-distributed among the different nets from which they have been derived. In particular, this exercise is well suited to re-constitute the Roman lines, and to reveal a great many ridgeways which tend to be suppressed on the topographical sheet.

It is generally known that prehistoric men circulated for the most part along the relatively open hilltops. Where the crests are very narrow it is possible that definite trackways were beaten out, but the early ways on the wider uplands should not be thought of as "roads" in the present sense. Very many of the ridge-routes, which in some form or other are incorporated in the present road system, owe their survival, if not their very existence, to medieval traffic. This point deserves to be strongly emphasized, especially in connection with the interpretation of town sites: many a so-called "gap town" was originally located, not at a focus of valley-ways, but where a ridge-route was interrupted by a crossing (cf. Chapter XIII). A not dissimilar case is that of the Anglo-Saxon *herepaths*, *harepaths*, or *hard ways*, occasionally named on the map. These, literally "army paths" but in fact surfaced or at least firm roads, run generally along the crests and show where overland movement was easiest in early historical times. Valley-ways are a later development: although they account for so much of the existing main-road system, they must not be allowed to confuse interpretation of origins.

The rectilinear Roman system and the irregular net of medieval and modern times are both guided by relief, but in different ways. Despite their long straight stretches and their small concession to details of landform, the Roman roads are remarkably well adapted to major physical features, as may be clearly seen on the ¼-in./mile maps. The Fosse Way, for example, runs near the foot of the Cotswold dip-slope, avoiding the more deeply incised valleys of the plateau to the north and the ill-drained claylands to the south. Passing through the Moreton Gap, the best defined break in the Jurassic hills for many miles in either direction, it continues below the main scarp-face but above the bottom of the Avon valley, which is floored with marly boulder clay. Post-Roman roads, tortuous as a whole, are at many points guided by minor topographical features but are also instructively related to the broader lie of the land, for example in clay country, where they are frequently seen to run along the very low divides. The manner of approach to obstacles, such as rivers, is especially informative, and well repays study in connection with the siting of towns: it is proper to inquire why the roads should make for a particular point in order to cross, rather than another in the same part of the valley.

A concluding general remark may be offered on the subject of nodality as expressed in the pattern of routes. Because roads are the most numerous of routes, they are the best able to show convergence on a particular focus; but it is a mistake to imply that a town has arisen or expanded because roads, as such, converge on it: usually the roads have become better defined and more frequented as the town has grown larger. It is inevitable that roads should reveal the nodality which is essential to all towns, but the nodality itself is a matter of situation rather than of connections.

The Pattern of Rural Settlement

Interpretation of settlement can be highly rewarding, if the interpreter will recognize the fact that, with few exceptions, the map attempts to show present distributions only. Whatever can be inferred, nothing is actually stated about how the observed patterns came into being. There is, for example, little direct evidence that the different parts of a town differ in age or in function, or that different elements in the pattern of rural settlement were introduced at different times. Here is at once the interpreter's task and his limitation.

The remainder of this chapter will be given over to a discussion of those various aspects of rural settlement which most closely affect map interpretation. Prehistoric occupance and the analytical study of towns are made the subjects of separate chapters, where they can be conveniently illustrated by reference to maps selected for the purpose.

Units of Rural Settlement. The development, stage by stage, of a given complex of settlement and routes is to be traced by the historian, the historical geographer, and the archaeologist; but the pattern cannot be perceived until the roads, buildings, historic and prehistoric sites have been mapped. To suppose that patterns, especially patterns of settlement, can be made out implies that habitations are grouped and distributed in characteristic and recognizable ways. With these the interpreter should be broadly acquainted. The units of rural settlement are the isolated farm, the hamlet, and the village. Small market towns are closely linked with their surroundings, both economically and socially, but basic functional differences compel them to be treated under a different head. Although there is continuous gradation through the farm-hamlet-village series, with the result that a strict classification is not always possible, it is nevertheless often found that a given stow or tract is dominated by one of these elements, or by more than one in a definite combination. In parts of the English

Midlands, for example, villages lie near the centres of their parishes with outlying farms around them; elsewhere the hamlet is dominant; elsewhere again, most rural habitations are disseminated single farms, as is finely illustrated on the O.S. Ireland 1/63,360, Sheet 169.

The fundamental distinction is that between nucleated settlement and dispersed settlement. The observed pattern need not, however, be the original pattern. It expresses merely the cumulative effect of a number of factors in the complex relationship of man to ground. The problem of interpretation is far from simple, and can scarcely be attacked unless certain principles are clearly understood.

Some environmental factors appear to have exerted a powerful but by no means exclusive effect on the form of settlement. We may remark, with Demangeon, that even relief and limited water-supply favour nucleation by limiting the effective choice of sites, whereas broken terrain and abundant water encourage dispersion. In this connection one may note the distinction commonly made between **wet-point sites,** where water is available in a relatively dry tract, and **dry-point sites,** for example, "islands" of relatively good drainage in a marsh. A common relationship between the siting of settlement and the natural water-supply is, however, not an invariable rule. Social and ethnic factors, although not yet well understood and rather uncertain in their effects, have undoubtedly influenced the form of some rural settlement. Demangeon considers the chief of them to have been the form of agricultural economy, which although itself open to the influence of the environment, appears to have been capable on occasion of determining the form assumed by pioneer settlement. Thus although "the unit of settlement on the English Plain was the village community," consisting in its purest form of a cluster of houses standing in the midst of its territory,[1] the Jutish system of land tenure and agriculture was associated with hamlet settlement in the lower Thames valley and in the Continental Angle.

It is no part of the present task to discuss the origin of the early field systems, the way in which they were linked with the feudal system of government and administration, or the effects on agricultural practice of improvements in tools and systems of cropping or stock management. The mere reference must suffice to show that the historical problem of rural settlement is exceedingly difficult and complex.

[1] H. C. DARBY, in *An Historical Geography of England Before A.D.* 1800. Edited by H. C. DARBY. University Press, Cambridge, 1936, p. 189.

To suppose that a crude and direct relationship exists between settlement and land is to be guilty of gross over-simplification.

The observed pattern of rural settlement in the English Plain has evolved, in large measure, from the pattern established by Saxon, Scandinavian, and contemporary pioneers. The evidence of place-names and Domesday Book proves the antiquity of many settlements, while Darby has shown that much of the forested low ground had been cleared before the Norman invasion. In other words, the conquest from nature of what is to-day the best agricultural land was, to an important degree, the work of the Dark Ages. There have of course been later changes. Some village communities were destroyed by a catastrophe such as war or plague; others were removed to make way for the sheep farming of the fourteenth and fifteenth centuries. Some new settlements have been established, elaborating the ancestral pattern. In the eighteenth and nineteenth centuries openfield working was finally superseded by wholesale enclosure, and new farms were built on the newly consolidated holdings.

Forms of Rural Settlement. These most recent enclosures are principally responsible for the combination, in many lowland tracts, of nucleated villages and outlying farms. It is important to recognize that the two elements date from widely separate periods. Where the village is the original settlement, the form is that of **primary nucleation,** while the farms represent **secondary dispersion,** i.e. a later re-distribution of population in single scattered dwellings or hamlets. Since the village survives, secondary dispersion has been incomplete. Dispersion is also possible as an original form, but is rather difficult to prove. Again following Demangeon, we may identify **old-established primary dispersion, intercalated dispersion,** and **recent primary dispersion,** in addition to the secondary dispersion already mentioned. Old-established primary dispersion is most appropriate to moorland, woodland, and mountain country, which is unsuited to openfield working by a village community and where potential grazing is more abundant than potential tillage. Intercalated dispersion results from piecemeal colonization, for example, during the Middle Ages, of the forests and wastes remaining between the cleared land of the villages. Recent primary dispersion is the form of relatively modern agricultural settlement, where single farmsteads have been established on the newly won land.

The problem of old-established primary dispersion arises in discussions of Highland Britain, where the systems of land tenure descend from Celtic times, never having been superseded by Romano-British or later practices. In these generally less hospitable and wetter tracts, the environmental factors thought to favour dispersion exert their strongest influence, especially where individual parcels of land have been reclaimed at the edge of the waste. Even here, however, investigation shows that primary dispersion cannot be taken for granted, no matter how widely disseminated dwellings may be at the present day. The custom of gavelkind in North Wales, and the breakdown of the rundale system of agriculture in Ireland, are now known to have assisted in dispersion from primary nuclei. Map evidence can be adduced for the complete dispersion of two Donegal villages between 1834 and 1903.[1] In view of these findings, one is well advised in dealing with rural settlement in Highland Britain to attempt nothing beyond a statement of existing distributions.

Parish Boundaries. It has long been known that a map of parish boundaries may bring out significant and useful facts. Despite numerous small adjustments, and some greater changes effected for administrative convenience, many boundaries remain substantially the same as they were when first determined. Hence it is possible to tell, in a general manner, what kinds of land were held by many of the original village settlements. For, although the same caution must be observed as in discussing the qualities of present agricultural land, one may justly recall that the medieval openfield systems tended to produce stereotyped methods of cropping and rotation, practised on the best arable land, and demanded in addition meadow, woodland, and common pasture. Where villages lay along a scarp-foot, there were obvious advantages in the division of land into long, narrow parishes running across the grain of the country, with meadow and woodland on the lowest ground, common grazing and probably woodland again on the hills, and the open arable around the village itself in the scarp-foot zone, which is typically one of favourable soils. Thus parish boundaries came to cross the boundaries of adjoining stows. A similar fact may be noted on parts of the fenland margin, where each group of villagers and each manorial lord wished to secure rights of exploiting part of the marsh. Where the differences in land quality were smaller, or were less apparent to the early settlers, and again where villages were founded in forest clearings, parishes tend to be more nearly hexagonal, although the actual boundaries

[1] See the work of E. ESTYN EVANS, cited on p. 113.

are usually irregular in detail. Examples of both forms in juxtaposition are given in the annexed Fig. 7 (*f*).

Rectilinear boundaries are uncommon. They occur in those parts of the fens which were drained late in historical times, where no landmarks had existed before reclamation, and in some mountainous tracts, where they are of limited interest or influence. Some, however, which run along Roman roads, neatly demonstrate that the road existed before the parish was delimited. Parts of Watling Street, for example, are used to mark county as well as parish boundaries.

Interpretation of Rural Settlement: Village Forms

The forms of individual villages, no less than their actual existence, may be influenced both by the environment and by the agricultural organization of the original settlers. As yet, the study of village forms is far less advanced in Britain than in some European countries, where the material is on the whole far more promising: large compact villages unaffected by secondary dispersion are easier to classify according to form than the small, shrunken agglomerations of rural England. In the interpretation of British maps, therefore, it is usually sufficient to distinguish elongated from massed villages. Where the forms are clear and detail is abundant, as on the 1/25,000 series, a number of subclasses can usefully be made out. Thus, the **elongated** or **linear villages** include the street-village, where houses line the street on either side, and the street-green village, of cigar-shaped plan and with an elongated central green. **Massed villages** are less easily subdivided, but one may separate those which are close-knit (with or without a central green) from those which are loose-knit or of indeterminate shape. Selected forms are illustrated, by village plans drawn from the O.S. maps used with this book, in Fig. 7 (*a–e*).

The interpreter should not attempt to classify all the villages on a given map according to this scheme, which is by no means comprehensive, but should seek to identify the dominant form(s) and to select a few marked exceptions for detailed examination.

Interpretation of Rural Settlement: Place-names

Place-name evidence is conveniently taken in conjunction with the pattern and rorm of rural settlement. Like the settlements themselves, the names have been modified in the course of time. Since the map records only the modern name (except at a few Roman sites), and, since place-name study is a highly specialized task, a map interpreter

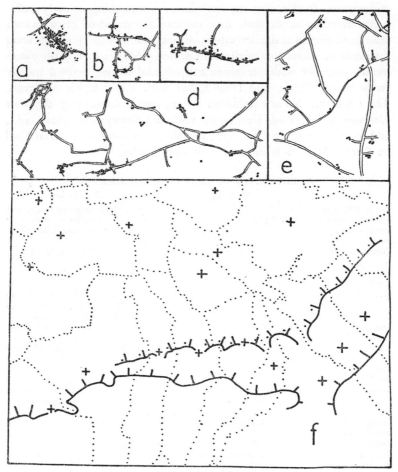

FIG. 7. PARISH BOUNDARIES
(Based, by permission, on O.S. maps)
Crown Copyright reserved

(a) Willersey, a compact village (O.S. New Popular 1/63,360, Sheet 144, 1039).
(b) Hagworthingham, a loose-knit village (O.S. New Popular 1/63,360, Sheet 114, 3469).
(c) Bishampton, a linear village (O.S. New Popular 1/63,360, Sheet 144, 9951).
(d) Rural settlement in hamlets (O.S. New Popular 1/63,360, part of Sheet 186).
(e) Dispersed rural settlement near Wexford (Survey of Ireland, 1/63,360, Sheet 169).
(f) Pattern of parish boundaries at the side of the Vale of Pewsey. Parish churches and the scarps of Chalk and Greensand are shown.

should attempt inferences only where certain common elements are widespread. In this way one may discover something of early settlement, avoiding at the same time most of the manifold errors which arise from guesses at the derivation of particular names. The following list contains a selection of the commonest elements in English place-names, together with meanings and original forms, derived mostly from Saxon, Norse, and Danish, but with a few Celtic additions. The Ordnance Survey publishes a very useful *Glossary of the Most Common Welsh Words Used on the Ordnance Survey Maps* (1949, 4d.), and formerly issued a *Glossary of the Most Common Gaelic Terms Used on Scottish Maps*, now unfortunately out of print.

A. ELEMENTS OF OLD ENGLISH ORIGIN

Element	Meaning	Derivation
berry, borough, borrow, brough, burg, burrough, bury	(primarily) fortified place	burh (dative singular *byrig*); but liable to confusion with Old English *beorg*, and Old Norse *berg*, hill
cester, chester	large city or town	ceaster, cæster; loan-word from Latin *castra*, camp, settlement
chipping	market	cīeping
cot(e)	cottage	cote
dean, den, dene	valley	denu; but may be confused with Old English *denn*, (i) lair of wild beast (ii) pasture for swine
don, dun	down, hill	dun; but liable to confusion with *denu* and *tun*
ea, ey	island; also "land in midst of marshes"	ēa, ēu, eig; also from Old Norse *ey*
field		
ford		
ham	generally "farm" or "estate"	hām; but liable to confusion with *hamm*, enclosed possession, fold
hampstead, hempstead	site of chief house of a farm or manor	hām + stede
harepath, herepath, hardway	literally "army path" but used generally of through-roads	herepæþ
hirst, hurst	(i) hillock, knoll, bank (ii) copse, wood—possibly originally "wooded height"	
holt	wood	
ing	often originally — *ingas*, "X's people"	
ingaham, ingham	the *ham* of X's people	
ley	originally woodland; later, clearing in woodland	lēah
port	town, especially with market rights and rights of minting	
stead, sted	place, position, site	stede, styde
stow	place, site	
strat, street,	primarily a road of Roman con-	strǣt

Element	Meaning	Derivation
stret, etc.	struction, later any made-up road	
thorp(e), throp	village or hamlet	þorp, þrop; but many thorpes were so named by the Danes
ton	wide range of meaning; primarily enclosed piece of ground, then enclosed land with dwellings on it, i.e. estate, manor, vill, village	-tūn; but possibly also from Scandinavian
wood	wood	wudu

B. ELEMENTS OF SCANDINAVIAN ORIGIN

Element	Meaning	Derivation
booth	originally shieling (centre for summer pasture)	both (Danish) buth(Old Norse)
by	village, town (Danish) homestead (Norse)	byr
ergh	see booth	
ey	island, etc.	ey
force, foss	waterfall	fors
garth	enclosure	garðr
gill	ravine, cleft	geil
ings	meadow-land, especially in marshy places (North-country dialect word)	eng
thorp(e)	a hamlet or daughter-settlement dependent on, i.e. colonized from, an older village	thorp
thwaite	clearing; but many thwaites date from the thirteenth and fourteenth centuries, the word having passed into local speech	þveit
toft	piece of land, homestead; often clearing	topt
ton	see under "Elements of Old English Origin"; sometimes from Scandinavian—tūn	

C. ELEMENTS OF CELTIC (CORNISH) ORIGIN

Element	Meaning	Derivation
pen	head, top, summit, promontory; but also possibly from Old English penn, pen or enclosure	pen
pol	stream (cf. Welsh poll); also possibly from Old English pōl and Welsh pw̄ll	a pool, deep place in a river
tre, trev	homestead, village, town; often hamlet	

Wooldridge has shown that three phases of Anglo-Saxon settlement can be distinguished, each associated with specific place-name elements: the *entrance phase* of skeletal infiltration to the areas of early settlement, the *expansion phase* of secondary colonization around and within the early settled tracts, and of territorial expansion by conquest, and the *terminal phase*, when the settlement plan was filled out and assumed for the time being a relatively static condition. Place-names are most informative about the entrance phase, which is recorded in many names of early form, including -*ing* names (where these are derived from names in -*ingas*), a large number of names in -*ham* and in the combinations -*ingaham* and -*ingham*. Naturally enough, these early elements are commonest on the eastern side of the country. Scandinavian forms occur widely on the north-eastern side of a line joining the Cheshire Dee and the Lea River, i.e. north-east of Watling Street. Norse elements are frequent on the western side from Cumberland to the Wirral, and also extend farther southwards along the coast; the rest of the last formed part of the Danelaw and Danish forms are expectedly frequent. In the western highlands, Celtic (including Gaelic) names are abundant along the old frontiers of conquest.

NOTES AND REFERENCES

Much information relevant to the subject of this chapter is to be found in—

H. C. DARBY. *An Historical Geography of England Before A.D.* 1800. University Press, Cambridge, 1936. (See especially Chapter V, *The Economic Geography of England, A.D.* 1000–1250, by H. C. DARBY, p. 165.)

Settlement patterns and forms are discussed in—

A. DEMANGEON. "L'Habitat Rural." *Comptes Rendus, Congrès Internat. de Géographie*, Cairo, 1925. Tome IV. Reprinted in A. DEMANGEON, *Problèmes de Géographie Humaine*. Colin, Paris, 1947, p. 153.

A. DEMANGEON. "La Géographie de l'Habitat Rural." Reprinted from *Ann. de Géog.*, 199 and 200, xxxvi, 1927, in *Problèmes de Géographie Humaine* (above), p. 159.

A. DEMANGEON. "Types de Peuplement Rural en France." Reprinted from *Ann. de Géog.*, 271, xlviii, 1939, in *Problèmes de Géographie Humaine* (above), p. 291.

W. PAGE. "Notes on the Types of English Villages and their Distribution." *Antiquity*, i, 1927, p. 447.

F. SEEBOHM. *The English Village Community*. Longmans, Green, London, 1883.

Seebohm's work contains much helpful material on the relationship between agricultural systems and the structure of the community. On this point, reference may also be made to—

C. S. and C. S. ORWIN. *The Open Fields, Oxford*. Clarendon Press, Oxford, 1938.

C. S. ORWIN. *A History of English Farming.* Nelson, London, 1949.
H. PEAKE. *The English Village.* Benn, London, 1922.

Accounts of certain processes which have greatly modified the cultural landscape occur in—

H. C. DARBY. "The Clearing of the English Woodlands." *Geography,* xxxvi, 1951, p. 71.
H. C. DARBY. "The Changing English Landscape." *Geogr. Journ.,* cxvii, 1951, p. 377.

See also—

M. W. BERESFORD. "The Lost Villages of Medieval England." *Geogr. Journ.,* cxvii, 1951, p. 129.

Individual studies include—

E. ESTYN EVANS. *Irish Heritage.* Tempest, Dundalk, 1945. (See p. 47 ff., Figs. 13 and 14, for evidence of rapid dispersion.)
E. Jones. "Some Aspects of the Study of Settlement in Britain." *Advancement of Science,* viii, 1951, p. 59.
B. M. SWAINSON. "Dispersion and Agglomeration of Rural Settlement in Somerset." *Geography,* xxix, 1944, p. 1.

In the study and interpretation of place-names, one should make use whenever possible of the relevant county handbook of the Place-name Society. The whole series has not yet appeared, however. A great deal of help is obtainable from—

A. MAWER and F. M. STENTON. *Introduction to the Survey of English Place-names.* (English Place-name Society, Vol. I, Part 1.) University Press, Cambridge, 1925.
A. MAWER. *The Chief Elements Used in English Place-names.* (English Place-name Society, Vol. I, Part 2.) University Press, Cambridge, 1924.
E. EKWALL. *The Concise Oxford Dictionary of English Place-names.* Clarendon Press, Oxford, 1951. (Contains a useful introductory study.)
ORDNANCE SURVEY. *Glossary of the Most Common Gaelic Words used on Ordnance Survey Maps.* (Out of print.)
ORDNANCE SURVEY. *Glossary of the Most Common Welsh Words used on Ordnance Survey Maps.* 1949.
These works have been freely drawn on in compiling the Table given above.

The scheme of land-use classification adopted by the Land Utilization Survey is set out in—

L. DUDLEY STAMP and E. C. WILLATTS. *The Land Utilization Survey*

of Britain; an Outline Description of the First Twelve One-inch Maps.
Land Utilization Survey, London, 1935, pp. 5–7.

The extremely great geographical value of the Soil Surveys will be conceded by all with experience of working over ground for which soil maps are published. The pattern of soil-distributions shown on the maps is complex, but complex reality is no excuse for neglect or scorn. Among the soil maps already available on 1/63,360 are Sheet 296 (Glastonbury) of the Soil Survey of England and Wales, which relates to part of the area represented on Sheet 165 of the O.S. series, and Sheet 22 (Kilmarnock) of the Soil Survey of Scotland, which refers mainly to drumlin country. Both of these maps are strongly recommended.

CHAPTER XII

RURAL SETTLEMENT STUDIES

It sited was in fruitful soil of old—Spenser

Maps: O.S. 1/63,360 (Seventh Series) Sheets 114, 144, 167, 186; O.S. Tourist Map, 1/63,360 (Lorn and Lochaber); O.S. 1/25,000, Sheet NC/76. U.S. Geological Survey, 1/62,500 (Pinal County (Arizona) Casa Grande Quadrangle)

1. Dominantly Nucleated

O.S. 1/63,360 (Seventh Series) Sheet 144 (Cheltenham and Evesham)

The area shown on Sheet 144 is dominantly one of nucleated rural settlement. There are towns, Cheltenham sizable and the rest small, as well as numerous scattered farms, but the village is the typical unit. This fact does not preclude differences between stows in the size and form of village or in the relation of settlement to ground.

To the east of the Cotswolds, that is to say roughly east of the Grid Line 16, numerous villages of no great size lie in the valley stows drained by the Windrush, Evenlode, and Avon. Many sites near the foot of hills obviously had the original advantage of water from springs, for example the three Rissingtons (1921, 1919, 1917) and the corresponding villages of Icomb, Westcote, Idbury, and Fifield on the eastern side of the same hill. Streams can be seen to head near, and to flow away from, the base of the slope, while the name Springhill Farm (2516) is significant. Villages of this kind are conveniently styled wet-point settlements. If the rocks forming the high ground were permeable throughout, a definite line of springs would be looked for at the geological boundary. Villages grouped around springs would then constitute spring-line villages or scarp-foot villages, according to whether emphasis were placed on relation to water-supply or relation to terrain as a whole. In this locality, however, the resistant rocks are variously permeable in themselves as well as being separated by clays, so that springs occur at various elevations on the sides of hills and in belts rather than in lines. The wells[1] of a single village may tap a number of water-bearing horizons.

Also in this eastern part occur villages on or very close to streams, particularly to the Stour, in valley-bottom sites. Halford stands where the Fosse Way crosses the river, but the remaining valley-bottom villages on the Stour appear to have little relation to the control of crossings: in the first place, not every village has its road bridge, while secondly, there are seventeen crossings of some kind in the 12 miles of valley between Tidmington (2638) and the confluence with the Avon. Evidently the difficulty of crossing was insufficient to concentrate traffic at a few points only. Mills and weirs show that these riparian sites had the advantage of potential water power, which was in due course developed and must have assisted the survival and growth of the mill-owning villages; but potential water power cannot alone account for the selection of the sites in question. Place-name evidence shows that the settlers were Anglo-Saxons. It follows that the stow was found generally suited to cultivation. Field investigation is required, since published geological maps are inadequate to the purpose, to prove that these valley-bottom villages are, in fact, sited on patches of low terrace. Faint pointers towards this conclusion are given by the sites of Halford (2645) and Tredington (2543), each in the inner side of a meander-loop: such siting confirms the suggestion of the contours that the Stour is ingrown, but there is nothing to show whether the ingrowth has been continuous or spasmodic.

The shortcomings of the topographical map are again evident a little to the south, where Stretton-on-Fosse (2238), Todenham (2436), the Wolfords (2434, 2635), and Barton on the Heath are sited on hills capped by sandy and gravelly drift, which provides a perched water-table and drier ground than the surrounding claylands. Only the "Heath" element in the last-mentioned place-name provides a dubious clue.

Along the north-western side of the Cotswolds wet-point settlements are strung out near the scarp-foot, from Mickleton (1643) to Great Witcombe (9114). They are linked by the Stratford-on-Avon–Cheltenham–Bath road, but particularly north-eastwards of Winchcomb (0228) tend to lie on one side of it or at a little distance. In this north-eastern part the typical village site occurs at the mouth of a combe, the short re-entrant valley of a scarp stream. In the field,

---

[1] Water-supply schemes are progressively reducing the number of small wells in use, but the historical argument remains unaffected.

Photograph: films, Aero Ltd.

(A) AERIAL VIEW OF THE MENDIP PLATEAU, WITH CHEDDAR GORGE (CENTRE)

Photograph: Aerofilms, Ltd.

(B) PART OF THE FENLAND, NEAR BOSTON, SEEN FROM THE AIR

Note the regularized Witham, the rectangular field pattern, and dispersed
settlement.

PLATE III

Photograph: Aerofilms, Ltd.

(A) AERIAL VIEW OF STOW ON THE WOLD

(B) PART OF MERTHYR TYDFIL: TERRACED HOUSING,
STEELWORKS, AND TIP-HEAPS

PLATE IV

Buckland (0837) and Stanton (0634) in particular seem to be almost enclosed by hills. Broadway, by far the largest member of the group, lies where the London–Evesham road descends the scarp-face; the influence exerted by traffic on this road on the growth of Broadway is well shown by the remarkable elongation of the village in the direction of movement.

In the dissected plateau stow of the Cotswolds, nucleated settlement avoids the tops of interfluves, and the small villages are located chiefly at valley-bottom sites as wet-point settlements, where roads cross the larger valleys, or near the heads of tributaries. Examples of the former class are Temple Guiting (0928) and Naunton (1123), lying within the incised valley of the Windrush, and of the second Notgrove (1020) and Aston Blank[1] (1219) near the heads of feeder streams. It is noticeable that some valley-bottom villages, narrowly restricted by the valley walls, have grown along the valley. Withington (0315) is especially interesting: the village extends in an arc across the Coln, in conformity with the shape of the meandering valley.

In the claylands flanking the Avon different factors operate. The scarp-foot settlements encircling Bredon Hill, and similar settlements associated with similar but smaller hills to the south, may be regarded as outliers of the main belt of scarp-foot villages, just as the hills themselves are outliers of the Cotswolds. For the rest, there is a noticeable tendency for villages to be sited on the higher rather than on the lower ground, as dry-point settlements. Among the clearest examples are Pebworth (1347) and Long Marston (1548), each on the crest of a low interfluve, and Aston Somerville (0438) on one side of a low spur. In reality this sub-edge country received a great deal of soliflucted material during the Pleistocene. The deposits are by no means without influence on the agricultural quality of the ground and on its suitability for settlement, but the topographical map fails to indicate either these or the true glacial deposits which are also present.

Close to the Avon the record is clearer. Physical interpretation has indicated that terraces are present. It is now seen that, on the flood-plain proper, buildings and roads are alike rare. Below Evesham, where the Avon describes great loops, nucleated settlements are systematically disposed on the intervening spurs: Charlton (0145), Fladbury (9946), Wick (9645), the town Pershore (9546), the hamlet Pensham (9444), Birlingham (9343), and Eckington (9241). The immediate neighbourhood of Fladbury illustrates particularly well the

[1] Locally called Cold Aston.

manner in which settlement and trackways tend to cease at the boundary of the flood-plain, as here defined by Oxton Ditch and Lench Ditch. A contrasted factor of siting is the navigability of the river, demonstrated by weirs and locks. A number of villages are placed where meanders impinge on the higher, firmer ground, so that deep water can be reached without crossing the flood-plain. Such sites are those of Wyre Piddle (9647) and Cropthorne (0045) in the reach just discussed, and of Bidford on Avon (1051) farther upstream.

Crossing-places below Evesham are differently placed from those above. In the lower reach Eckington Bridge (9242), Pershore Bridge (9545), and Jubilee Bridge (0045) lie near points of inflexion of the great river loops, that is to say at about where the direction of curvature is changing. Since the flood-plain alluvium is disposed in crescents on the inside of the loops, crossings at such points are made between the tips of adjacent crescents and involve the minimum traverse of ill-drained ground. Upstream of Evesham the valley bottom has been more extensively cleared by the sweeping meanders, with the result that a wider and more regular belt of flood-plain must be traversed. The ford at 065470 and the two road bridges (1052, 1453) carry roads which descend meander-spurs where the ground is at least a little dryer than on most of the flood-plain. In addition, place-names along this reach show that a number of settlements grew in association with fording-places—Salford Priors, Bidford, and Welford.

Although many of the villages in the area of this map sheet are small, the most casual inspection in the field leaves no doubt that, as stated at the outset, rural settlement is dominantly nucleated. Because of their smallness, little useful comment can be made on the form of villages. Most are rather formless agglomerations,[1] a well-defined shape being imposed only in exceptional cases by close adaptation to the qualities of the site. An influence not to be read from the map was the decline of the Cotswold production of wool and woollen cloth, a decline which has been reflected in the declining population of the plateau.

The result of secondary dispersion, on the other hand, is easily perceived. If it is assumed on the basis of place-name suffixes that many of the existing settlements were established by Anglo-Saxons, and on general grounds by way of corollary that openfield agriculture was practised for many centuries, it appears probable that the single farms are in large part the result of movement outwards from pre-existing

---

[1] *Haufendorfer* of continental writers.

agglomerations.[1] The assumptions and the inference are in fact justified by historical evidence. As in many other respects the map record is incomplete: not every farm which exists in the field has the word "farm" attached on the map, besides which it is common to find some farmhouses within the villages themselves. Nevertheless, the available information is sufficient to show the presence of outlying farms, for example, four named in the parish of Stretton on Fosse (2238) and four also in Aston Blank parish (1219).

Quite apart from the naming of farms, it goes without saying that a widely cleared, well-peopled countryside of this kind is very largely in tillage or pasture. The precise mode of land use, which is itself liable to considerable change in response to economic pressure, can be read only when it is indicated by a symbol. The hangers of wood on steep slopes may well represent the remnants of a former extensive woodland cover in the Cotswolds, although many small patches with rectilinear bounds and lying on flatter ground are likely to be plantations (cf. Stanway Ash (0832)). Again, in formerly wooded country it is often found that a park is partly ringed by narrow woods, as at Northwick (1636), Trafalgar Farm (2911), and Bembro (1027). The last two have evidently been put to agriculture while all three may well represent early clearance of woodland granted by the Crown to an individual. Recent clearance appears in the combination of the symbols for trees and for rough grazing, for example, in the kilometre square 1226; but Brockeridge Common (8838) is a more doubtful case because of the name and is likely to be covered by heath or scrub.

It is well known that the Vale of Evesham is noted for specialized cash crops, market-garden produce and orchard fruit. Such specialization is due to a whole complex of factors which lie in part in the proper field of the economist. The geographer engaged in map interpretation should confine himself to remarking the facts shown on the map, in this instance the considerable areas under orchards, and to the tacit assumption that the local climate, soil, and aspect are favourable to tree-fruit growing. The chief concentration of orchards is around Evesham, except on the lowest ground, which has the double disadvantage of poor drainage and of liability to frost[2]; extensions from this central area run up and down the Avon. Where the orchards are

---

[1] This dispersion was of course the concomitant of enclosure.
[2] As might be expected, some orchards do lie within frost-pockets (see the work of RAYMOND BUSH cited at the end of this chapter).

more scattered it is seen that (for obvious reasons) they tend to abut on metalled roads. Away from the river, or more properly from the terrace spreads, the scatter of orchards is less dense, but continues up to and includes the line of scarp-foot villages, with incipient penetration of the upper Stour valley. The abrupt cessation of orchards at the scarp-foot line is a fair sign that here marked agricultural and physical boundaries coincide.

2. Dominantly Dispersed

O.S. 1/63,360 (SEVENTH SERIES) SHEET 186
(BODMIN AND LAUNCESTON)

The very frequent place-name element "Tre-," with the less common "Pen-" and "Pol-" show that the pattern of rural settlement here has developed not from Anglian, Danish, or Scandinavian origins, but from Celtic. Much of Highland Britain, including this part, resisted the militant settlers of the Dark Ages, so that the array of villages representing original nucleation, with intervening farms representing secondary dispersion, so familiar in parts of the English Plain, is not to be sought on this map. At the same time it may well be emphasized that the wide dissemination observed is not necessarily the effect of primary dispersion. It is true that the generally impermeable rocks and the heavy rainfall of Highland Britain made water-supply no great problem, and that therefore wet-point settlements grouped round springs are unlikely to occur in numbers, but the matter is far more complicated than this. Until the agrarian economy of Celtic times is better understood, it is best to accept the present fact of dissemination as it stands, noting at the same time that several recent studies point to the law of gavelkind as a powerful factor in causing dispersion in parts of the Celtic west.

Disseminated rural settlement may be dominated either by the hamlet or by the single farm. In the area of Sheet 186 the hamlet appears typical to the north-east of Bodmin Moor, while separate farms are most numerous in the south, say, south of Grid Line 65. The hamlets are characteristically sited high up on the sides of tributary valleys, close to the subdued tops of the interfluves but at the same time in sheltered positions. True valley-bottom sites have rarely been selected. The many single farmsteads of the south, being presumably placed somewhere near the centres of their respective land, occupy less obviously selected sites, but in the field are nevertheless seen to take advantage of folds of the ground too small to be represented by the available contours.

The major part of Bodmin Moor may be taken as unimproved rough grazing on heath or bog. Single farms occur on the flanks and avoid the highest ground. From the manner in which rectilinear patches free of the moorland symbol are interspersed with land which is still heath, one may infer that piecemeal enclosure and improvement has gone on (cf. "New Closes" (2071)). If this is so, the single farms established in the cleared areas would represent primary dispersion, in the familiar guise of squatter settlement on the margins of poor land. It is noticeable that in prehistoric times the higher parts were more hospitable than they now are: besides many tumuli and various arrays of standing stones, there are groups of hut circles and one "Ancient Village" (2376) to prove former extensive habitation.

Any attempt to explain the location of villages in this area by local nodality is bound to fail. In the first place, as nearly all are so diminutive that they lie very close to the ill-defined division between hamlet and village, any factors tending to increase their size seem to have operated but feebly. Secondly, there appears little to choose between the road connections of most villages and those of a large number of hamlets. The fenced roads, which cover the whole area, except for Bodmin Moor, in a close network, are mostly classified as "Under 14 ft. of metalling, bad" or "Minor roads," and some villages are served by no roads of higher grade, for example, Treneglos (2088), St. Clether (2084), and Cardinham (1268). On the map, the two obvious differences between villages and hamlets are that the former are named in larger and different type—which, indeed, is the easiest means of identifying them—and that each has a church. It would appear, therefore, that in this area the settlements to be recognized as villages are ecclesiastical centres, and presumably also centres of local administration, of parishes where most dwellings lie away from the centre. It is for the historical geographer and others to discover whether, when the parishes were delimited, settlement was more strongly nucleated.

Dispersed agricultural settlement extends right to the coast, with diminutive villages at intervals among the farms and hamlets. As there is very little low ground immediately behind the shore, small groups of buildings find themsleves somewhat precariously placed along the base of the cliff (Portwrinkle (3553), Downderry (3154)) or uncomfortably confined in small youthful valleys (Polperro (2151), Polruan (1251)). Pentewan (0247) also clings to the foot of the slope behind, probably because the flat ground is too sandy for building. The improved harbour here, like those at Charlestown (0451) and Par (0752), which has rail connections, evidently provide outlets for the china clay fields north of St. Austell.

In conclusion one may turn to the Fowey to remark the very small agglomerations characteristically located at the head of the lesser inlets: Lerryn (1457), Penpoll (1454), and Pont (1451). Because of the smaller volumes of the tributary streams these sites are relatively little affected by silting, and at high tide can be reached by fishing craft and small coasting steamers.

3. Rural Settlement in the Fenland

O.S. 1/63,360 (SEVENTH SERIES) SHEET 114
(BOSTON AND SKEGNESS)

Each of the several kinds of stow represented on this map is clearly distinguished from the others by differences of physique, of drainage, of form and distribution of settlement, and of the road nexus. However complex the relation between man and land, the sharp differentiation observed here leaves no possible doubt that the terrain has exerted a powerful influence on the history and nature of occupance: the effect of occupance on the ground is no less clear.

The only land above 50 ft. O.D. lies in the north, outside the fenland boundary. This stow has already been noted as one of fairly weak rocks, generally impermeable and heavily dissected into country of many wide valleys and small divides. The irregular parish boundaries and the winding roads show early occupation and unplanned development. Nevertheless a definite connection is to be observed between the form of the ground on the one hand, and the location of settlement and the course of roads on the other. The roads avoid valley bottoms, except to cross a stream, running instead near the foot of the valley walls or along the crests of divides; villages also show a general preference for the high ground. It is of the greatest importance to note that the finer details of location would amply repay intensive study in the field, for the place-names Gravel Pit Hill (3669), Sandhill Farm (4364), and the Brick and Tile Works at Hundleby (3866) mean that marked local differences are certain to occur in the qualities of the waste-mantle and of the soils developed thereon. Although the soil survey of Britain is not yet far advanced, enough is known to justify the statement that, unless variations of soil can be taken into account, the pattern of rural settlement cannot be fully understood. Since a vast quantity of fundamental data must thus be awaited, and since in any case soils are not recorded on the topographical map, the interpreter needs to discuss rural settlement with these reservations in mind, and should not fail to support the general argument by drawing attention to such facts as those indicated.

Four groups of tumuli (4072, 4171, 4371, 4471) testify to early penetration of possibly Bronze Age date. The road with long straight stretches from 4075 to 448697 invites inquiry, especially as it is continued by a mile of field road near Burgh le Marsh (494657). The straightness suggests a Roman origin; but the nearest site actually described as Roman lies some miles to the south near Wainfleet All Saints, where the ancient Salt Works locate the shoreline of some 2,000 years ago. Place-names ending in -by, which are very common, show that Scandinavian invaders settled here in force, apparently displacing, subjecting, or destroying earlier Anglo-Saxon inhabitants, whose traces remain, for instance, in the place-name terminations—ham (for example, Greetham, 3070) and -ingham (for example, Hagworthingham, 3469). Names in -ton are less helpful, since, where Scandinavian and Anglo-Saxon forms occur in association, this termination may be of mixed derivation.

As in the Cotswolds and the Avon valley, studied on Sheet 144, primary nucleation may be taken as highly probable, with Dark Age villages sited on patches of drier soils above the wooded valleys. The outlying farms would then once more represent secondary dispersion. Another mode of expansion may be interred from the thorpes (for example, Mid Thorpe and Far Thorpe, 2673 and 2674), which are likely to have been founded as daughter-settlements some way from the original village.

On the seaward side, this northern stow is bounded by the fen, which is thrown into prominence, on the map, by its sub-rectangular pattern of roads, parish boundaries, and drainage channels. (In the field the physiographic boundary is sharply and narrowly defined.) This regularity in the features of occupance (Plate IIIB), the scale of the drainage works effected, and the obliteration of most of the natural water-courses are sufficient to indicate that reclamation came relatively late in historical times, even were the general facts less well known. It is permissible to take the ubiquitous name "fen," together with the flatness and very low altitudes, as presumptive evidence of the nature of the soil, which must be developed largely on fen peat. One may pass rapidly over the form of settlement, which is characteristic of tracts reclaimed by major drainage operations: individual farms occur at intervals on the roadside, where the risk of flooding or waterlogging is least, or, more rarely, at a short distance from it. The pattern is one of recent primary dispersion. Nucleated villages occur only where firmer ground rises through the fen deposits, as at Stickford (3560), Stickney (3457), and Sibsey (3551). The -ey element shows that at one time two of these sites appeared as "islands" in the fen. Differences of level, as shown by the spot heights, are very slight but significant: the main road linking the three villages takes an irregular line, while the houses are distinctly grouped into street-villages.

East and north of Wainfleet and Burgh le Marsh the ill-drained belt is narrower than to the south-west, and less obviously modified by the work of man, but here, too, a contrasted stow intervenes between the low hill country and the coastal belt.

It was observed in the discussion of physical distributions that the coastal belt itself comprises two tracts, one of salt marsh already reclaimed or in process of reclamation, and one of firmer ground where settlement is old-established. In the stows of reclaimed marsh, between Gibraltar Point (5558) and Freiston Shore (3943), between Freiston Shore and the Welland, and between the Welland and the Nene, the pattern of occupance recalls that of the fenland: regular drainage channels, straight roads, and the single farms of recent primary dispersion are again observed. Progressive reclamation is attested by the "Old Sea Bank" (4955) and the "Roman Bank" marked in several places (but possibly later than Roman, despite the name), as well as by the "Old Marsh" and "New Marsh" (5158, 5257). The Roman Salt Works have been mentioned before. Note also the strip of marsh represented above high-water mark.

The next tract inland, between the salt marsh and the drained fen, stands little above the sea. It is nevertheless one of firmer ground, which is well settled with old-established villages and a complex net of local roads, and which retains some elements of the natural drainage system. Individual stows in this tract vary somewhat from the general pattern. In the southernmost, immediately south of the outer belt of reclaimed marsh between the Nene and Welland outfalls, the road network is more open and rather more regular than in the others, while the largest settlement is a hamlet. Between Wainfleet and the extreme south-west of the area mapped, the belt of firm ground is as much as five miles wide in places. It is traversed by reclaimed valley bottoms and inlets which formerly connected the marsh of the shore-line with the fen behind: Bicker Haven (2533), The Haven (3540), Friskney Low Ground (4454) and the neighbouring Wrangle Low Ground, and the mouth of the Steeping River. Scandinavian place-name elements such as *toft*, *beck*, *wick*, and *thorpe* indicate one period of conquest and settlement. The *-ey* of Friskney bears witness to the working distinction made in early times between the better and the less well-drained land. The several "Low Grounds," "Commons," and "Fens" must have been held communally by the villages after which they are named, under a medieval system of agronomy. Many minor place-names imply a close relation between man and land, and a keen appreciation of the varied qualities of the setting, for example, the common "dyke," Fishmere End (2837), Freiston Shore where the firm ground reaches the sea, the *ings* which are, in this tract, patches of meadow in the marshland, and the name "hill" given to very low rises. After what has previously been said, it is unnecessary to stress the facts that the settlement pattern results from primary nucleation, with secondary (or perhaps intercalated) disper-sion, and that villages tend to straggle along almost imperceptible crests.

Between Wainfleet and Burgh a stow of firm ground provides a link with the hilly tract in the north-west. Once more, it is marked by irregular roads and some nucleated villages. The pattern recurs north of Gibraltar Point, where the dryer ground abuts directly on the sea. Salt marsh is replaced by a sandy beach, with which is asso-ciated the only new element that requires attention, i.e. the signs of recent growth in the villages of Ingoldmells and Chapel St. Leonards. Planned streets of modern layout at 570692 and 559731 indicate that these two small centres have shared, to a limited extent, in the modern growth of seaside resorts which has been responsible for the present size and form of Skegness.

4. Rural Settlement in Glaciated Highland

O.S. Tourist Map 1/63,360 (Lorn and Lochaber);
O.S. 1/25,000, Sheet NC/76

Both the distribution and the form of settlement in glaciated mountains are powerfully, although not exclusively, influenced by the setting. It is in the nature of such tracts to include large negative areas, devoid of soil, very steeply sloping, inaccessible, or climatically formidable.

Within the occupied parts, however, there is room for considerable variety, according to the qualities of the ground, the system of agriculture practised, and the relations of the tract with other tracts outside. A general concentration of settlement in the valleys is inevitable. One may also safely postulate for earlier times an almost complete dependence on subsistence farming, in which the relative importance of livestock and tillage varied with the abundance of good land and the qualities of the climate. Since good tillable land is generally scarce, one may look for a selective concentration of rural settlement on favourable sites.

A marked contrast between adjacent sites is characteristic of glaciated highlands, and ensures that some influential facts of the environment can be clearly read. The problem of aspect, however, demands careful analysis for a complete solution. While the broad difference between the northern and southern sides of a glacial trough is obvious enough, Garnett has shown that significant differences of aspect between the sites on one side only can be discovered from the map when certain techniques are employed. As the required treatment is somewhat lengthy, the reader is referred to the works cited at the end of this chapter for a description of method and results; but it must be borne in mind that, unless analysis of this kind is attempted, questions of aspect can be discussed only in general terms.

The various environmental factors of location are likely to operate most powerfully near the upper limit of settlement, where conditions are most difficult. Local differences of aspect serve to modify the general limitation imposed by low summer temperatures, severe winters, and long duration of snow cover, which are themselves partly determined by height and latitude. Some Alpine villages are situated far up the valleys, at heights which in Scotland would be on or above the peaks. In the difficult tract represented on Sheet 47, the sparse settlement is not confined merely to the valleys but nearly everywhere to the valley bottoms, and the problem of distribution is to that extent simplified.

Rural settlement occurs both in dispersed and in nucleated form, but where grouping occurs it is dissimilar to that of the English Lowlands. Trislaig (0874), Blarmachfoldach (0969), South Garvan (9977), and Inverroy (2581) may be taken as examples. In each the houses straggle along the glen. Trislaig has already been identified as occupying a patch of raised beach. The houses lie along the old shoreline, with cleared land in front and open moor rising behind. Assuming this to be an agricultural settlement, one may suppose that the limited area of flat ground, with its soil developed from raised beach deposits, is likely to carry tillage crops and hay, while livestock is pastured on the lower hillside. This is so in actuality (1950): the organization is that of **crofting,** the form of subsistence agriculture proper to the remote Highlands. However, even though the environment imposes strict limits on the possible organization of farming, marked differences are possible within those limits, and it must not be assumed that the crofting system holds good everywhere. One may perhaps repeat the caution that the topographical map shows only the distribution of buildings and the extent of cleared land, with, at some sites, physical features likely to provide tillable soil. Furthermore, the map alone cannot show how greatly the system of crofting may have been modified: in its fullest development, crofting involves an economic isolation and a low standard of living which are both rare to-day. A further characteristic, again not to be read from the map, is the black house, a single-storeyed chimneyless building containing a family of crofters at one end and the livestock at the other. The type form may be modified by the addition of chimneys, and by the complete partitioning of the two ends, but the general structure is distinctive enough, as at Trislaig.

At South Garvan there is apparently a less abrupt change from flat to slope, and enclosures have been cleared and improved as high as the 100-ft. contour. It would appear from the irregular moorland boundary (better shown at Blaich (0377)) that the land has been taken in piecemeal. At Blarmachfoldach the clearance has, in total at least, been more regular, extending upwards from the stream bank well past the line of houses to a smooth fence at the edge of the moor. Inverroy is different again. There are two lines of houses, one at a sharp break of slope between the valley wall and the valley floor, which also coincides approximately with the limit of moorland, and one below the main road, at the edge of an alluvial valley flat or **haugh.**

Alluvium provides other sites capable of cultivation in deltas and delta-fans, which must be numerous where so many ungraded streams are well supplied with rock-waste. Deltaic sites at the heads of lakes or at the mouths of large tributaries are identified without difficulty. At many of them, buildings lie near the apex where natural drainage is good, with easy access to, and command of, the whole cone, and safe from flood (cf. Fassfern (0279)). Much of the dispersed settlement is also located on sites of this kind, but the cones are frequently too small for the map to show (cf. Guesachan (8879), obviously on deltas built into Loch Shiel, with Tighnocomaire (9469), where there is actually a small **corrom** or delta-fan).

A scale of 1/63,360 is able to reveal that some houses are considerably larger than those of the crofting settlements. The contrast in size, and also in plan, is well shown by Sallachan (9863) and the Crofts of Sallachan to the east of it. The map does no more than record the numerous large "Houses": the social order which produced them is a subject for historical study, except that one may regard them as a likely outcome of an aristocratic or squirearchical system.

The relation of certain Highland settlements to the land on which they lie is illustrated in more detail on the O.S. 1/25,000, Sheet 29/76. Nearly all the habitations shown are comprised in five groups: Armadale (7864), Kirktomy (7463), Swordly (7363), Farr (7263), and Bettyhill (7062). On this map, where field boundaries are shown, it is at once seen that the houses in Armadale are strung out along the lower hillside, with small enclosures carved out of the moor above or running down to the stream and the shoreline below. The moorland symbol within some enclosures indicates either that the part of the land proved intractable, or that it has been allowed to revert, for example because of a decline in population. At Kirktomy and at Farr, buildings lie roughly at the break in slope between the steep hillside and the flatter low ground—a relationship already observed on the 1/63,360 sheet. Bettyhill is the only group which has expanded sufficiently to require an attack on the hilltops. Here the subdued summits at c. 300 ft. O.D. have been enclosed and to some extent cleared in the significantly named Newlands: the spread of clearing has evidently been associated with the establishment of dwellings at this higher level. One might suggest that the vigour of Bettyhill, by comparison with the other groups, has something to do with its situation on the main road (cf. the presence of an hotel). Because of the expansion, it is not clear whether Bettyhill may not include more than one original group. Farr, Armadale, and Kirktomy are more truly representative of a settlement form indigenous to the Scottish Highlands, the **clachan**—a loose agglomeration of precisely the kind seen here, but often no more than a small, loose-knit hamlet. On this sheet the name "clachan" appears once only, applied to a small group of buildings at the eastern end of the modern Bettyhill.

To explain the origin of the clachan, it would be necessary to take account not only of a former dependence on subsistence farming, but also of the former social structure of clans, and of family groups within the clans. Thus it is seen that even here, in country where physical circumstances impose strict limits or severe difficulties on land use, the pattern of rural settlement cannot be understood without appeal to additional factors.

5. Recent Primary Dispersion

U.S. GEOLOGICAL SURVEY, 1/62,500 (PINAL COUNTY (ARIZONA) CASA GRANDE QUADRANGLE)

The pattern of rural settlement here is geometrical. Systems of numbered squares, in which the rural habitations lie, relate to the arbitrary division and allocation of land at the time of settlement by white men: each square is a **range**, 1 mile by 1 mile in size, with a block of thirty-six squares making up a **township**. The town of Casa Grande and the small, rather loosely grouped smaller settlement of Chiu-Chiuschu in the south show a tendency to develop converging roads, while other short lengths of road lead to wells, but in general the rectangular pattern of land holdings is repeated in, and emphasized by, a rectangular net of minor roads. Most houses lie by the roadside. With such an arrangement nucleation can scarcely begin, for, if a square block of four ranges is owned or held by four farmers, the largest possible grouping—at the central crossroads—would include only four farms plus the dwellings, if any, of farm-workers. The factors militating against nucleation here are comparable to those responsible for the primary dispersion noted in drained fen.

In this climate, proved to be arid by the nature of the landscape, and without a supply of water for irrigation, farming is certain to be pastoral. The wells are needed for domestic water-supply and for watering stock. They tap the water-table in the deposits of the alluvial plain, which is fed by percolation from intermittent streams and occasional rainstorms. Note the absence of wells on the pediment in the south-west, where settlement may have been deterred by the lack of ground-water in a very thin cover of rock-waste. Below the Sacaton Mountains, on the other hand, superficial deposits seem to extend across the foot of the pediment, for wells have been sunk as high as the 1,500-ft. contour. It should be remarked that, although water-supply is possibly the most pressing of all problems for settlers in this tract, the special qualities of the water-table in the alluvium and the use of modern techniques of well-sinking result in the almost complete

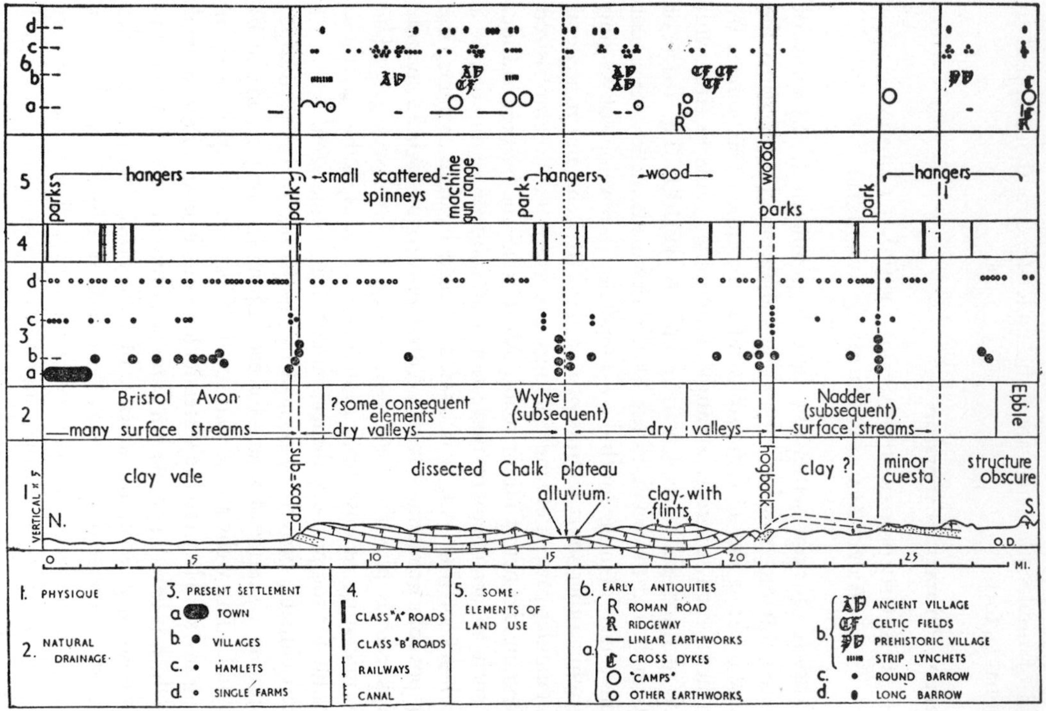

Fig. 8. A Transect Chart

(Based, by permission, on part of O.S. New Popular 1/63,360, Sheet 167)

absence of anything comparable to the wet-point settlements studied elsewhere.

6. The Transect Chart

O.S. 1/63,360 (SEVENTH SERIES) SHEET 167
(SALISBURY)

Structure, surface, and human occupance are seldom wholly uncon-nected, however complex the relationship may prove to be. The transect chart provides a useful and graphic means of sampling and summarizing the various distributions, and of revealing their simil-arities and contrasts. Because the similarities tend to be prominent in the finished chart, it is necessary to repeat the caution against crude determinism. The first aim of the map interpreter is to perceive and define the association, for example, between settlement and landform, and to discover, within the limits of his data, how closely the one is adapted to the other. Man is everywhere the active partner, limited, aided, or excluded by land, but never compelled.

The transect chart was developed for use in presenting the results of intensive local survey, in which, among other things, rainfall, vegeta-tion, and agriculture can be fully studied. A transect chart constructed from a map is more limited in scope. Suitable headings are: profile of relief, with inferred geology where possible; physical features; nature drainage; surface utilization; settlements and communications; prehistoric occupance.

The chart is constructed in the manner of a graph, with the profile drawn across the bottom and other information arranged above in columns, against the appropriate headings (Fig. 8). The profile refers, of course, to a single line on the ground: additional matter may be drawn from a belt of country, for example that defined by arbitrary lines parallel to the line of profile. In the example given, the profile is drawn from north to south along the Grid Line 94. Further informa-tion is taken from the area included between the lines of easting 90 and 98. A north-south transect is chosen as crossing the grain of relief (and of structure) approximately at right angles. Where a large feature is crossed obliquely, as, for example, the Wylye valley, it and its associated features of settlement, etc., are "projected" on to the line of profile and noted in the relevant column.

Since the chart is in itself a tabular descriptive summary, the facts presented need not be elaborated. The reader is strongly advised, however, to check the chart against the map in order to understand precisely how the data have been obtained.

NOTES AND REFERENCES

On the nature and analysis of aspect and related matters, see—

R. BUSH. "Frost and the Fruitgrower." *Geography*, xxx, 1945, p. 80.

A. GARNETT. "Insolation, Topography, and Settlement in the Alps." *Geogr. Review*, xxv, 1935, p. 601.

A. GARNETT. *Insolation and Relief.* Institute of British Geographers, Publication No. 5. George Philip, London, 1937.

The significance of scarp-foot and dip-foot belts, and of river terraces, is demonstrated in—

S. W. WOOLDRIDGE and D. L. LINTON. "The Loam-terrains of South-eastern England in their relation to its Early History." *Antiquity*, vii, 1933, p. 297.

S. W. WOOLDRIDGE and D. L. LINTON. "Some Aspects of the Saxon Settlement in South-east England Considered in Relation to the Geographical Background." *Geography*, xx, 1935, p. 161.

This question is also referred to in—

S. W. WOOLDRIDGE. "The Anglo-Saxon Settlement." Published in *Historical Geography of England Before* 1800. Edited by H. C. DARBY. University Press, Cambridge, 1936, p. 88. (This essay discusses the relation between place-name elements and the phases of penetration.)

Drainage of the Fenlands is reviewed in—

H. C. DARBY. "The Draining of the Fens, A.D. 1600–1800," Chapter XII, p. 444 ff., in *Historical Geography of England* (above).

Specimens of the transect chart, together with the method of construction from field survey, may be found in—

C. C. FAGG and G. E. HUTCHINGS. *An Introduction to Regional Surveying.* University Press, Cambridge, 1930. (See especially pp. 112, 115.)

C. A. SIMPSON. "A Venture in Field Geography." *Geography*, xxx, 1945, p. 35.

Dispersion of settlement in the Celtic west is described in the works of EVANS and JONES listed at the end of the preceding chapter. The studies of settlement form there specified could be usefully supplemented by—

H. THORPE. "Some Aspects of Settlement in County Durham." *Geography*, xxxv, 1950, p. 244.

H. THORPE. *The Green Villages of County Durham*. Institute of British Geographers, Publication No. 15. George Philip, London, 1951, p. 153.

CHAPTER XIII

TOWNS: SITE, FORM, AND SITUATION

What is the meaning of this city?—T. S. ELIOT

We have come to regard the town almost as an organic unit. Its origin, where we can trace it, is almost completely controlled by very definite and very local circumstances. An early growth beyond that of its immediate neighbours is usually to be associated with a quite definitely superior site. The modern road, the canal, and the railway focused on such sites, and each such artificial addition became a factor in the town's growth often more potent than any local physical circumstance.—RODWELL JONES

MAPS: O.S. 1/63,360 (SEVENTH SERIES) SHEETS 114, 144, 165, 167; O.S. 1/25,000, SHEETS SY/18, SO/00; O.S. TOURIST MAP 1/63,360 (LORN AND LOCHABER); O.S. IRELAND 1/63,360, SHEET 169, ETC.; U.S. GEOLOGICAL SURVEY, 1/62,500 (PINAL COUNTY (ARIZONA) CASA GRANDE QUADRANGLE)

As Darby has pointed out,[1] there seems to have been little continuity between the towns of Roman Britain and those of later times. The manner in which urban life renewed itself in the Dark Ages is complex and obscure, but it may be said that "long before the Norman Conquest a force had begun to operate which was ultimately to give the English borough its most permanent characteristic, i.e. that of a trading centre."[2] Whatever other functions towns discharged, marketing remained a principal concern during several hundred years, when most people lived in the country and urban growth was slow.

Effects of Re-growth

The extent and form of the pre-industrial towns are still recognizable in the towns of to-day. Although the fabric has been renewed, the plan survives in the compact massing of buildings and in the narrow,

---

[1] H. C. DARBY. *An Historical Geography of England Before A.D.* 1800. Edited by H. C. DARBY. University Press, Cambridge, 1936, p. 214.

[2] *Ibid.*, p. 215.

irregular streets. The close-packed inner part, especially well marked where the old town was confined by a wall, may be styled the **core**. The remarkable increase in the country's population during the last 150 years has been effectively an increase in urban population, for some 80 per cent of the present total live in towns. This almost explosive growth is expressed on the map in the **integument,** that part of a town which surrounds the core. Streets and buildings are more widely spaced than in the centre, forming a separate and distinctive pattern.

Not in every town is a core of medieval growth surrounded by a later integument. A number of minor centres have neither been industrialized nor converted into dormitories: they remain, as it were, all core. Towns which are almost entirely the product of industrialism seem to be all integument, but it is usually practicable to separate the regular, crowded inner part with its nineteenth-century layout from the more open and varied later portion.

Form

Identification on the map of the distributional patterns within a town is part of the study of town **form,** with which interpretation is most simply commenced. The problem involves much more, how-ever, than the separation into integument and core: the integument may be subdivisible, to some extent, according to function. Now the main present functions of a town cannot be considered without reference to past function, site, and situation. All of these items are closely and complexly interrelated, but should not be confused: the interpreter should be quite clear at all times which of them is being discussed. So much regrettable confusion has in fact arisen in the past that a few explanatory comments may be given.

Function

The **function** of a town implies its whole life and work, social and economic. Various classifications of towns according to function have been proposed, but if past functions are taken into account function becomes confused with site, while if attention is confined to present conditions the resulting classification is likely to be unsatis-factory. The division into towns of extractive industry, towns of manufacturing industry, and towns of service industry[1] is too general; that into manufacturing, retail, diversified, wholesale, transport,

---

[1] See R. E. DICKINSON. *City Region and Regionalism.* Kegan Paul London, 1947, p. 45 ff., for a reference and comments.

university, resort, and retirement centres[1] tends to conceal the fundamental variety of urban life. Furthermore, it can hardly be disputed that the functional classification of towns must have a statistical basis which the map cannot provide. Thus it appears that the interpreter is best occupied, not in trying to affix a single functional label, but in discovering something of the structure and internal diversity of a given town. It is in this latter task that a classification of functions is required, in order that the different parts of a town may be properly described. The following list, adapted from Aurousseau, may serve the purpose—

Production.
Communication and transport.
Marketing.
Residence.
Recreation.
Administration.
Culture.
Defence.

When different functions have come to be localized in different parts of a town one may expect the map to show which are the chief manufacturing, residential, and recreational areas, as well as the main facilities of transport and communication. All these tend to lie within the integument. Administration, culture, and marketing are more typical of the core, but as a rule the only positive map evidence consists in the names of individual establishments or the distinctive representation of public buildings. A defensive role belongs to the past and should be considered under the head of site. In any case, medieval towns were commonly walled for defence, whether or not they were founded as strongholds or had castles.

The question of function arises in another way. Just as there is no universally clear distinction between hamlets and villages, so villages grade into towns. Recent studies have revealed that some agglomerations fail to discharge certain functions proper to towns in general, although they have urban administrative status. For purposes of work with O.S. maps, it is necessary to rely on the form of lettering employed in place-names to suggest which of the smaller centres can be classed as towns. On the current New Popular Edition of the 1/63,360 map the styles of lettering are not yet entirely standardized, but, since the

---

[1] *Ibid.*, p. 23, Footnote 2, for reference to authorities and brief comments.

smallest administrative area for which capital letters are used is the Urban District, all places with their names in capitals have been taken as towns for the purposes of this discussion.

Situation

All towns are nodal. The convergence of roads seems merely to respond to the guidance of physical features, but the interpretation of nodality nevertheless is not always easy. Under the heading of **situation** the map interpreter can attempt to define and describe— subject always to the limitations of the map—the geographical setting. The economic and social relations of a town, which may be regarded as external functions, are (like internal functions) a matter for statistical treatment. In map interpretation they must be taken largely for granted. The task of the interpreter is to state how and why the town is physically accessible, how the converging routes which express nodality are related to the form of the ground, and how the town is placed in relation to the boundaries of stows and tracts. For obvious reasons, small market towns are often centrally placed in the areas they serve, but larger collecting and distributing centres are more typically peripheral. This is obviously true of a great port or a major collecting-centre like Winnipeg, but a number of lesser towns are also significantly placed near the boundary of contrasted tracts, where dissimilar products can be marketed.

Many nodal points lie at the focus of a sheaf of valleys. The crude and obvious interpretation is that the town site is a node of valley-ways, but it is often at least as probable that the early routes followed the crests of divides, avoiding damp and wooded valley-bottoms. Ridge-routes would, of course, converge on the same point as the later valley-roads.[1] Similarly with many "gap towns": admittedly such a town commands the gap, on which modern roads converge, but formerly movement overland may have been principally *across* the gap, along the line of the high ground on either side.

Site

When the **site** of a town is examined, two things should be looked for: the **nucleus** around which growth has taken place, and the manner in which the growing town has adapted its structure to the form of the ground. On a small-scale map the nucleus alone may be

[1] The author is indebted to Dr. H. C. Brookfield for suggesting Hertford as a leading example.

visible. Consider the frequent case of a small country town lying at
one end of a river bridge: the bridgehead, commonly with the addition of defensive works, constitutes the nucleus; but, when the term
"bridgehead town" has been applied, interpretation is not much
further forward. Careful examination will often reveal, or at least
suggest, why, if the river had to be crossed in the locality, the bridge
should stand where it does instead of half-a-mile or so upstream or
downstream; that is, in what way the point selected is superior to
others available near by. Much can usually be done towards interpreting the advantages of the particular site, but none of these can in
themselves explain the growth of a town. The question that should be
asked is: assuming that a town is to grow somewhere in this neighbourhood, which is the likeliest site, and why?

Similar treatment should be applied to a port. The physical setting,
however advantageous, can in no sense account for the existence of a
port, which is due to powerful economic and historical factors. On
the other hand most (but not all) large ports are clearly located in
close relation to geographical features; but, since few ports have been
deliberately founded as towns, it is often difficult to find the nucleus
around which they have grown, modern harbour works having
destroyed or obscured the original advantage of position. If a port is
of any size, its site to-day will probably combine favourable with
unfavourable factors, for example, tidewater far inland with little
room for expansion, which the interpreter should try, as far as possible,
to perceive.

On the 1/63,360 and comparable or smaller scales it is not always
possible to make out in detail any correspondence between the form
of a town and that of the ground, especially where parts stand on
river terraces which do not show well on the topographical map. The
attempt should always be made, however; it is rare in unplanned towns
to find no evidence whatever of what may be called "preferential
growth" in certain directions. Where a town is functionally differentiated, a rough correspondence is often found between the functional
subdivisions and the type of ground on which they are located. Thus
the study of site returns to that of functions and structure, with which
this discussion opened.

*   *   *

The maps already used show forty-seven towns, with part of a forty-
eighth, Bristol. There is more than enough material to illustrate

specifically the principles set out in the earlier part of this chapter, so that it will not be necessary to study all the towns in detail. Since, however, no dominantly industrial town is wholly represented, Sheet SO/oo of the O.S. 1/25,000 Series has been selected in addition, for an interpretation of Merthyr Tydfil.

The Small Market Town

Small market towns raise few problems of interpretation, except that, paradoxically, maps on the smaller scales cannot show whether or not a market survives; but, even if cattle and produce markets have ceased to operate, the market square is part of the nucleus around which growth has taken place, and the towns continue to discharge the functions of marketing in the wider sense of retail distribution to the surrounding countryside. By definition, towns of this kind are not greatly industrialized, and have not been greatly affected by the urban spread of modern times. Nevertheless, the interpreter is well advised to look for factories, which not infrequently occur. Some are related to an essentially local industry, for example, flax mills or processing plants for dairy produce; others are outposts of the major industry carried on in a neighbouring large centre, for instance, the leather works in several market towns of the Midlands; others again are the result of decentralization of industry, a complex economic process greatly stimulated by the recent war.

In or near the easternmost part of the Cotswolds (O.S. 1/63,360 (Seventh Series), Sheet 144) there are six small country towns: Chipping Campden, Shipston on Stour, Moreton in Marsh, Stow on the Wold, Northleach, and Burford. Although the plan differs from one to another, they have in common their compactness and lack of integument. Their sites bear a family resemblance to the sites of neighbouring villages, but their situations are more highly nodal.

Chipping Campden (1539), whose market function is recorded in its name, is centrally placed amid a group of villages which, like the town, occupy original wet-point sites. The large number of villages within a short radius of Chipping Campden is associated with the convergence of the two scarps, facing respectively east and north-west, and with the outlying scarp of Ilmington Hill, for most of the villages in question are located at the scarp-foot.

Moreton in Marsh and Stow on the Wold lie on the Fosse Way at nodes of cross-routes. If the official classification of roads is disregarded, the convergence of routes is found to be far more pronounced than the map at first suggests. The situation of Stow is especially instructive, for the town is sited on a hilltop approached from all sides by ridge-ways (Plate IVA). The road from Evesham and Broadway runs along the plateau top east of the headwater valleys of the Dikler; that from Tewkesbury via Stanway on the western side crosses only two valleys. There seems to have been an alternative to the second route through Winchcombe, across the Windrush near Guiting Power (0924) and thence eastward to Stow, but as a through-road this has been super-seded by the main road from Cheltenham, A.436, which is in part only a ridgeway and which makes more difficult crossings of the Windrush and Slaughter Brook valleys. East of the Fosse Way two ridgeways on either side of the Hazelford Brook valley run northwards to unite near Wyck Beacon (2020), whence the route continues across the col between the valleys of the Evenlode and Dikler. The main road from Oxford comes in from the east along the flank of Chastleton Hill, traverses a narrow part of the valley bottom, and mounts to Stow along the side of St. Martin's Hill. Although the roads from Bledington (2422) and Evenlode (2220) are not ridgeways they do not at least keep to the lowest ground, and are in any event less direct than those previously mentioned. Moreton in Marsh is very differently sited from Stow, lying on low ground where the Oxford–Evesham road crosses the Fosse Way. The immediate approaches cannot naturally take the form of ridgeways, in the ordinary sense, but are nevertheless distinctly related to the low divides of clay country.

Northleach (1114) offers an interesting contrast with Moreton and Stow, both of which stand on the Fosse Way whereas Northleach stands to one side. The site is in a valley bottom with a natural water-supply, between dry tabular interfluves. The town has grown east-wards and westwards along the valley, apparently from a nucleus near the church; the central cross-roads lie at the intersection of the Burford–Cheltenham–Tewkesbury road, A.40, with what is now a minor road from Bourton on the Water (1620) through Farmington (1315), branching at Northleach to Chedworth (0512) and Coln St. Denis (0811). It seems likely that at one time the less direct road was preferred to the Fosse, possibly because of easier gradients, for example, in the stretch between Northleach and Bourton.

Besides standing to the side of the Fosse, Northleach is also off the ridgeways. The significantly named Salt Way, running southwards from Evesham, passes about a mile away on the south-west; the road from Burford, instead of descending into the valley at Northleach, could continue to the north, rejoining the modern Cheltenham road at Puesdown Inn (0717). Thus Northleach is less directly nodal than might at first appear; its nodality arises, in part, from the fact that several ways pass close by, so that Northleach provides an approximation to the several cross-roads.

Shipston on Stour (2540) further illustrates the effect of movement along other roads than the Fosse Way. No nucleated settlement occurs on the Fosse itself, either at the crossing of the Chipping Campden–Banbury road, or at that of the road from Stratford on Avon up the Stour valley towards Oxford. Instead, a small market centre has arisen where these last two intersect, at one end of a bridge over the Stour. Note at Shipston, as at Chipping Campden, isolated buildings which appear to stand in the main street. These are probably covered market halls or exchanges. Burford (2512) resembles Shipston in controlling a river crossing, but also possesses an ancient priory, which may well have encouraged early growth and have assisted Burford to outpace the alternative crossing-settlement at Barrington, 3 miles upstream. The road system south of the Windrush well repays close study.

Enough has now been said to illustrate the fact that, within the class of small towns, great variety of setting is possible within the limits of a single tract of country. That is why the interpreter should deal with each such town on its merits, refraining from hasty classification and using to the full the information obtainable from the map.

The six towns discussed are very small and show few or no signs of recent growth. Melksham and Devizes, in the north-west of the area of the O.S. 1/63,360 (Seventh Series) Sheet 167, although by no means big towns, are larger than the previous examples and appear to be expanding. The characteristic openwork pattern of recent suburban housing appears on the eastern side of Devizes, in the kilometre Grid Square 1061, while Melksham is spreading to the south-east and north-east. Note also at Melksham the rubber factory. It is difficult to imagine that the town offers specific advantages for rubber manufacture—it is far more probable that the general factors of rail transport and a potential labour-supply were relied on when the industry was established.

Some country towns, without being industrialized, have yet grown fairly vigorously in modern times. They often serve as the economic centres of whole tracts or of large stows and their wider influence is not infrequently recognized in place-names (cf. Salisbury and Salisbury

Plain, Evesham and the Vale of Evesham). They are more markedly
nodal than the smallest towns, and in addition usually occupy distinctive sites, for their eminence dates from medieval times when they
were strongholds of defence, noted ecclesiastical centres, or both at
once; but a town which stood very high in the medieval urban
hierarchy, for whatever reason, may have experienced very little re-
growth, for example, the cathedral town of Wells and the neighbouring
Glastonbury with its renowned Abbey (O.S. 1/63,360 (Seventh Series)
Sheet 165). We are concerned at present not with these, but with
towns of comparable antiquity and former size which have developed
vigorous modern functions of industry and trading.

Salisbury is a case in point (O.S. 1/63,360 (Seventh Series) Sheet 167).
The nuclear area includes the cathedral; the core is approximately
defined by the very densely built-up southern part of the present
town, with an outlying portion in the angle of confluence between the
Avon and Nadder. Outside the core there has been considerable recent
growth towards the north-west, in the Pembroke Park area, and
towards the north in the direction of Paul's Dene. On the eastern side
also a more open pattern of streets and buildings can be seen, between
the core and the railway. As no marked industrial development
appears to have taken place it seems that the modern growth of
Salisbury is related to its situation, for the town is well placed to serve
a large number of rural settlements in a tract where no other town
exists. Both site and situation illustrate the contrast between the conditions of Roman and post-Roman times respectively. The Roman
roads, now in large part disused or reduced to the condition of bridle
ways, radiate not from Salisbury but from the earlier centre of
Sorbiodunum (Old Sarum). The modern Salisbury lies at the focus
of two sets of roads, those running along the crests of interfluves and
those following the valleys. Since nucleated settlements are concentrated in the valleys it is the valley-ways that best express the
nodality of Salisbury as a market centre, even though the easiest
approaches in the early days must have been along the ridges. The
frequent elements -*ton*, -*ford*, and -*bury* in the place-names of the valley
settlements are associated with Saxon penetration. Thus, although the
observed pattern of settlement and communications belongs to post-
Roman times, it has evolved from an original pattern of considerable
antiquity—a fact which serves to emphasize the utility, in a discussion
of Salisbury, of separating the core of the town from the integument.
The recent growth of the latter corresponds not to an increase in rural

population but to closer and more extensive commercial links between the town and its environment.

Ports

Except for Bristol, which appears only in part on one of the selected maps and will not be discussed, the ports available for study are small.

Bridgwater (O.S. 1/63,360 (Seventh Series) Sheet 167) stands at the lowest crossing of the tidal River Parrett. Roads converge on the bridge from the west, running across the broken hill country, and also from the east where they are more directly guided by the belts of dry land amid the fen. Since there is a relatively short traverse of fenland between the extremity of the Polden ridgeway and the river crossing at Bridgwater, it is readily understood that the town has considerable nodality in respect of movement by land, quite apart from any traffic on the Parrett.

The site of Bridgwater may usefully be compared with that of Combwich (2642). Both settlements are based on firm ground which approaches the river on the western side, and both originally possessed small natural inlets to serve as harbours. Combwich is several miles nearer to the open sea, and presumably has the longer period of high water, but can scarcely have provided a crossing in the very early days when fording not bridging was the rule. Furthermore, the natural drainage of Pawlett Hams, across the river from Combwich, appears likely to have been considerably worse than that of the ground opposite Bridgwater.

The small core of Bridgwater is almost surrounded by integument, wherein ribbon building may be identified along all the radiating roads. Modern expansion has been industrial, for in addition to the railway-carriage works one observes a number of factories alongside the Parrett, from 305384 in the north to 320353 in the south-east. It seems that the navigable river has been more influential in locating factories than either the railway or the canal. Since no factories are named or otherwise described, apart from the railway-carriage works and the brick and tile works at Chilton Trinity (3039) it is impossible to suggest what the dominant industry might be. The many patches of inland water on the eastern side of the town might be flooded clay-pits, as they are at Chilton Trinity, but might equally well be gravel workings.

Few of the facilities of a small port can be adequately represented on a map of this scale: the 1/25,000 Series enjoys a better scope. Since, however, factories are located on the Parrett it may be inferred that wharves have been constructed along the river banks, providing accommodation additional to that of the small dock. The canal leading out of the dock would not appear to have been a great success, since factories avoid it. The more useful railway link is secured by spurs to the dockside and to the quays on the east of the river in Castle Field.

In many respects Boston (O.S. 1/63,360 (Seventh Series) Sheet 114) resembles Bridgwater. It also is an estuary-head port, with obvious local nodality. Narrowly confined between the old fen on one side and the former estuarine marsh on the other, the Boston crossing of the Witham carries roads which converge along the broad lanes of firm ground, as well as that running southwards along the "islands" of Stickney and Sibsey. Although the shoreline has been pushed seaward for a considerable distance by reclamation within historical times, the Witham is still tidal up to Boston bridge. Since a canal takes off at Dogdyke (2155) the regularized Witham above Boston must be navigable for canal-boats, but unlike the Parrett is not flanked by factories. The modern growth expressed in the integument of Boston is to be associated with industrial development on the southern side of the town, near the small rail-served dock and also on the west of the river. Here no factories are named or described, but the two electricity transmission lines suggest that a power station may be located at 335431.

Like Bridgwater, Boston serves a rural hinterland: hence their relatively small size; but, just as Bridgwater surpasses Combwich, so Boston is larger and better connected than Wainfleet All Saints (5059). The general setting of Wainfleet is broadly comparable to that of Boston, but the former now lies more than three miles from tidewater on a smaller river than the Witham. Whatever historical factors may have operated, it is clear enough that as a port Wainfleet suffers grave physical disadvantages. Indeed, it has been effectively reduced to the status of a small inland market centre, located at a river crossing.

Wexford (O.S. Ireland, 1/63,360, Third Edition, Sheet 169) is another small port in a rural tract. Since the map was last revised in 1898, it can hardly be expected to record a large integument. Very little can be read from the map of port facilities, which appear to be restricted. They may possibly be represented by the jetty immediately downstream of the road bridge, together with the large buildings on the seaward side of the single-track railway. Undoubtedly the port of Wexford is unsatisfactory in some ways—probably because of too shallow water at low tide—for an outport has been established at Rosslare Harbour on the open coast. As Wexford seems very little industrialized, and as the cargo traffic of small ports is not usually too urgent to await a suitable height of tide, one may infer that the rail-served pier at Rosslare Harbour is designed for passenger traffic.

Other specialized ports on the selected maps include Kinlochleven and Fort William (O.S. Tourist Map, 1/63,360 (Lorn and Lochaber)), and Par and Charlestown (O.S. 1/63,360 (Seventh Series) Sheet 186). Each of the first pair has a deep-water pier, connected by rail with an aluminium factory, whence it would appear that bauxite is probably brought in by sea. The second two are Cornish ports which serve as outlets for the china clay field of Hensbarrow, north of St. Austell. They are too small to rank as towns.

Also in the area covered by Sheet 186, Lostwithiel (1050) and Fowey (1251) well exemplify a relationship of settlement to ria which is so common as to be properly regarded as typical. Lostwithiel is sited where roads converge on the crossing of the deep valley (cf. the place-name "Bridgend" at the eastern side). The main road from Liskeard is a ridgeway, which secures gentle gradients by skirting the heads of southward-flowing streams, and passes over the Fowey river at the (present) tidal limit, i.e. at the lowest point which could be crossed with relatively little difficulty. An east-west road nearer to the coast would involve many bridges and steep hills, and would approach the tidal Fowey where it is much wider. The town of Fowey, although provided with two ferry services, is not primarily a crossing-place, but a coastal settlement with a sheltered, deep-water harbour, directly connected on one side of the ria only to the town at the ria-head. An interesting modification of this association of towns with rias occurs on the Looe, which is again represented on Sheet 186. The river mouth is so narrow that bridging was not unduly difficult: in consequence East and West Looe combine the functions of bridge-town and port, and there is no settlement of any size at the ria-head. The principal road crossing of the Looe valley, however, is still located well inland, near Liskeard.

Resorts

Most resorts of this country lie at the seaside, for which reason they may conveniently be discussed next. Whereas the nucleus of a port may be regarded as an inlet, or as a conveniently sheltered portion of shoreline, the nucleus of a seaside resort is the central part of the front. The actual beach did not, as a rule, constitute a factor in the growth of a resort before an efficient system of sewage disposal had been acquired; but whatever its individual peculiarities of location and history, a seaside resort is usually distinguished by being sited on the open shore, and by possessing far more integument than core since it is largely a product of the last century, or even of the last fifty years.

Weston-super-Mare, Clevedon, and Burnham on Sea (O.S. 1/63,360 (Seventh Series) Sheet 165) may be contrasted in respect of site with the port of Bridgwater discussed above. Burnham, indeed, might be more aptly considered in relation to the small neighbouring town of Highbridge, a crossing-place and minor port on the River Brue. All three resorts are characterized by a relatively open pattern of streets and buildings, with very little sign of industrialization. All have golf links; Clevedon has one pier, Weston two. None is served by an inland waterway, nor does the railway approach the waterfront.

The considerable spread of building along the southern flank of Worlebury Hill, on the northern side of Weston-super-Mare, illustrates a typical development of resorts where suitable ground is available. The hillside is a "desirable residential area." The same phenomenon is illustrated in greater detail, although on a smaller scale, by Sidmouth (Sheet SY/18 of the O.S. 1/25,000 Series), where detached houses are scattered over the eastern side of the valley.

Clevedon and Weston each have a small core where the buildings are compactly massed; Burnham, lacking a comparable centre, appears to be of more recent growth, although the fact is not very clearly illustrated on the 1/63,360 map (cf. however the representation of Skegness on the same scale (Sheet 114): there can be no doubt that this resort has grown recently as well as vigorously, for no core of dense, older building is to be found).

When non-industrial inland centres display small cores and large integuments resembling those of seaside resorts, the leading probabilities are that the towns in question are also resorts, for example, spas, or that they function as dormitories. The fact offering itself for interpretation is once again the great extent of residential building. Although spas, as such, are no longer fashionable, they may have survived as residential or resort towns of a specialized character. Cheltenham (O.S. 1/63,360 (Seventh Series) Sheet 144) is one such.

Although its history can only be guessed at, the map indubitably represents a town with a large, unindustrial integument very similar in cartographic appearance to the outer parts of flourishing seaside resorts.

Large Towns

As was made clear in the early part of this chapter, the large modern town performs many functions. The towns discussed so far, simply because all are highly specialized and none is of more than moderate size, have been conveniently treated under summary descriptive headings, but it has already been observed that a useful distinction can be made between the inner (commercial) and the outer (mostly residential) portions. The core of Clevedon, for example, is identical with the shopping centre. The resorts of very recent growth, and the very small market towns, provide apparent exceptions, but maps on a larger scale (for example, 1/10,560) would show that in them also the central part is more densely packed than the outer, while a survey of urban land use would reveal the functional differentiation.[1] The next example provides more complex material. While it does not illustrate the large, fully diversified, "general-purpose" modern town, it combines extensive industrial and commercial areas with residential districts of two distinct kinds.

An Industrial Town

O.S. 1/25,000, Sheet SO/oo (Merthyr Tydfil)
On this scale the form of the town is very clearly shown. The core consists of the compact mass of buildings and narrow streets lying within the bend of the River Taff, in the north-east of the kilometre square 0405. The nucleus seems to have been located near the church at 050048. Early growth was probably responsible for the tongue of close building which fringes the main road to the north-east, but most of the expansion has undoubtedly been associated with the working of coal and iron ore, and with the manufacture of iron, which are so abundantly attested by the pits, levels, works, and spoil-heaps (Plate IVB). The development has been remarkably asymmetrical, and considerably guided in direction by the form of the ground: Dowlais (0607) is based on a broad spur between two small but deeply incised valleys, while Georgetown (0406) occupies part of the flat valley floor

---

[1] Functional maps of towns may be consulted at the offices of many planning authorities.

of the Taff. Despite the irregular outline of the whole, certain general conclusions are easily reached. Some quarters, for instance, that on the valley side south-east of Pen-y-bryn Water Works (0507), include an older and particularly compact element, but consist chiefly of the regular streets of terraced houses which are a typical product of rapid urban growth in the nineteenth and early twentieth centuries. With slight modifications, this pattern is repeated in much of Dowlais and in the Taff Valley both to north and to south of the core. That part of Merthyr immediately east of the main railway station, spreading north-eastwards up the hillside to Thomas Town, appears certainly to have been built later than the railway. A concentration of public buildings (shown by solid black) immediately north of the station suggests that some important cultural and administrative functions are discharged here, but the more easterly portions are less easy to interpret. On higher slopes where the land is free of industrial waste, or in valleys beyond the older residential quarters, one may note the wider, curving streets of suburbs constructed in the twentieth-century manner, as, for example, in the kilometre square 0508. The plan of these streets still has a certain geometrical uniformity, in contrast with the irregular scatter of large, detached houses on the hill flank above Cefn-coed-y-cymmer (0308).

The industrial functions of Merthyr Tydfil can be interpreted with unusual clarity. It is evident from the numerous old coal levels and old ironstone levels that, at least in the first days of industrial development, gently dipping seams of coal and beds of iron ore were worked in adits not by shafts. The Taff, and the Cynon in the next valley to the west have been incised into productive Coal Measures not violently disturbed by earth-movements and containing economic bands of ironstone. The presence of ironworks, as opposed to steelworks, indicates either that manufacture was established early, or that the local iron ore proved unsuitable for the acid Bessemer process which came to dominate steel manufacture from about 1860 onwards. The very numerous abandoned coal workings would also suggest early exploitation and relatively small individual concerns. The fewer but large pits now in work may be located by means of the notation on the map, by a characteristic pattern of railway sidings and pithead buildings (usually small), and by their association with active spoil-banks; for derelict tips are symbolized by hachures, while those still in use are shown by stipple and usually carry at least one line of rail. The features in question can be seen at Cwm Bargoed Pits (086060).

Ironworks require much larger buildings and more elaborate systems of railway lines (cf. those on the southern side of Dowlais at 065074). The huge quarries in the north, on the flank of Morlais Hill (0509) and elsewhere, appear to provide limestone, whose obvious destination

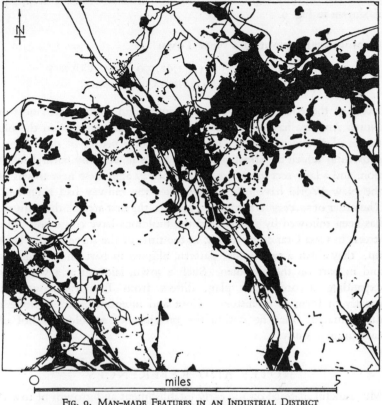

FIG. 9. MAN-MADE FEATURES IN AN INDUSTRIAL DISTRICT
Roads, railways, canals, buildings, quarries, and tip-heaps shown in solid black
Based, by permission, on Sheet SO/00 of the O.S. 1/25,000 Map)
Crown Copyright reserved

is the smelting works, for the highest ground hereabouts is marked, on the map, with the symbols for rocky edges and rock-strewn ground which have been encountered on the maps of Carboniferous Limestone country. One might, perhaps, advance the very tentative suggestion—justified, in point of fact—that the rock quarried is indeed the Carboniferous Limestone, which would, therefore, seem to dip southwards under the Coal Measures.

The exploitation of minerals, the tipping of spoil, the construction of works, and the expansion of towns have vastly transformed Merthyr Tydfil and its environment. Simple inspection of the map gives a powerful impression of the extent of this transformation, but its extent can be fully appreciated only by means of selective mapping, as shown in Fig. 9.

Geometrical Layout of a New Town

U.S. GEOLOGICAL SURVEY, 1/62,500 (PINAL COUNTY (ARIZONA) CASA GRANDE QUADRANGLE)

Many of the younger towns in the central and western provinces of North America have come into being very differently from the old towns of Western Europe. Instead of a long period of slow urban growth in which the street plan evolved, as it were, by natural selection, and a later recrudescence in the railway age, these new towns of the New World have often arisen after the railway had been laid. The order of succession has been reversed: the first arrival, the railway, has been followed by streets, and the buildings have come last. The streets in Casa Grande were not, at the time of the survey, fully built up; they form a rectangular pattern, aligned in part on the railway and in part on the meridian. Such a town, laid out as a whole or expanding according to plan, differs from European towns as greatly in form as in history. Core and integument are no longer differentiated: they lie within the province of sociological not of cartographic study.

NOTES AND REFERENCES

Much useful material on the early establishment and growth of towns occurs in—

H. C. DARBY (Editor). *Historical Geography of England before A.D. 1800.* University Press, Cambridge, 1936. (See especially Chapter V, "The Economic Geography of England," A.D. 100–1250, by H. C. DARBY, p. 214 ff.)

The classification and functions of towns are discussed by—

M. AUROUSSEAU. "The Distribution of Population; a Constructive Problem." *Georg. Review,* xi, 1921, p. 567.

R. E. DICKINSON. *City Region and Regionalism.* Kegan Paul, London, 1947.

R. E. DICKINSON. *The West European City: A Geographical Interpretation.* Routledge and Kegan Paul, London, 1951.

A. E. SMAILES. "The Urban Hierarchy of England and Wales." *Geography*, xxix, 1944, p. 41.

The economic relations of towns with their surroundings are attracting much notice at the present time. Among the papers which have so far appeared, the following may be cited—

R. E. DICKINSON. "The Distribution and Functions of the Smaller Urban Settlements of East Anglia." *Geography*, xvii, 1932, p. 19.

A. E. SMAILES. *The Urban Mesh of England and Wales.* Institute of British Geographers, Publication No. 11. George Philip, London, 1946, p. 85.

A. E. SMAILES. "The Analysis and Delimitation of Urban Fields." *Geography*, xxxii, 1947, p. 151.

Many individual studies have been made from time to time. The following is a very brief selection—

H. C. BROOKFIELD. "Worthing: A Study of a Modern Coastal Town." *Town Planning Review*, xxiii, No. 2, July, 1952, pp. 145–62.

E. JONES. "Tregaron, A Welsh Market Town." *Geography*, xxxv, 1950, p. 20.

S. J. JONES. *The Growth of Bristol.* Institute of British Geographers, Publication No. 11. George Philip, London, 1946, p. 55.

M. J. WISE. "Some Factors Influencing the Growth of Birmingham." *Geography*, xxxiii, 1948, p. 176.

CHAPTER XIV

PREHISTORIC OCCUPANCE

For monuments as for men, position is everything.—BALZAC
The laws of probability apply only to large numbers.—(Statistical axiom)

MAP: O.S. 1/63,360 (SEVENTH SERIES) SHEET 165
(WESTON-SUPER-MARE)

ON the bounds of archaeology the map interpreter must tread with care. Excavation and dating are the task of the field archaeologist, who makes use of a great body of material which the topographical map cannot record, and who is able to subdivide prehistory minutely. Map interpretation of prehistoric features depends on a fraction of the evidence that actually exists. It can take no account of artefacts but must rely on earthworks, and only on those earthworks which have survived, have been identified, and are represented on the map. These are the facts employed in an attempt to discover which parts of the land were occupied by man in each of the great cultural stages of prehistory.

The Question of Dating

The special maps of the Ordnance Survey, such as the Map of Neolithic Wessex, naturally raise no problems of dating, but the standard topographical map shows remains of very different age on the same sheet. The help afforded by distinctive notation is very limited. Roman sites and remains, where they are represented, are named in a special type—
UPRIGHT SANS SERIF CAPITALS on the New Popular One-inch map, although policy is now to employ **EGYPTIAN TYPE** for this purpose. Pre-Roman antiquities are shown in 𝔒𝔩𝔡 𝔈𝔫𝔤𝔩𝔦𝔰𝔥 𝔱𝔶𝔭𝔢, those of post-Roman date in 𝔊𝔢𝔯𝔪𝔞𝔫 𝔱𝔢𝔵𝔱.

On the New Popular Edition the difference between Old English type and German text is not always clear, but the 1/25,000 Series is wholly successful in this respect.

Fortunately for the purposes of interpretation, the nature of the remains is usually clear from the name or from the symbol, or both. Archaeology gives exactly the lead required in showing that each great class of earthworks is likely to belong to a certain one of the broad divisions of prehistoric and early historic times. The classes of earthwork, the cultural stages, and approximate dates applicable in Lowland Britain are summarized in the accompanying table. It must be stated as emphatically as possible, that the table has very little value in the classification of a single feature. There is, for example, no justification for referring a particular round barrow to the Bronze Age, but where a number of round barrows occur in a given tract of country it is highly probable that they are of Bronze Age date. The more numerous and closely grouped the barrows, the greater the probability. In dealing with prehistoric evidence, the interpreter should concern himself first and chiefly with *groups of features* not with isolated examples, that is to say, with the signs of undoubted and effective occupance.

The classes of earthwork listed differ widely in purpose. A few brief remarks are called for to relate each to the life of its period and to point its precise significance. The following paragraphs are by no means intended as an adequate review of prehistoric time in Lowland Britain, for which the reader should consult the useful elementary texts listed at the end of the chapter, but are meant to show how the broad relation of man to ground altered from period to period. A study of prehistoric distributions is in fact, to a large extent, a study of changing geographical values.

Neolithic Antiquities

In Neolithic times, the earliest from which earthworks are known in this country, agriculture was already being practised by people living in hill-villages. The organization was probably one of semi-nomadism, with tillage subordinate to pasture. It seems certain that the climate was more oceanic than it is to-day, and the water-table in uplands based on permeable rock—the Chalk in particular—is thought to have stood higher than it now does. Although the downlands carried timber they were much more easily penetrated than the lowlands, which, except for sandy outcrops and river terraces were, as a whole, damp, ill-drained, and densely forested. The soils of the open hilltops were deep enough and fertile enough for primitive cultivation, and movement was easiest along the ridges. There was little pressure of population on the best areas, and in any event

Neolithic men were ill equipped to clear or to cultivate the low-lying claylands, which, indeed, remained forested for many centuries. The commonest evidence of Neolithic occupance consists in **long barrows,** the characteristic mound of ceremonial burial. Long barrows are not numerous, partly because only a limited number were built by a small population, but partly also because some have been exploited for building-stone and in that manner destroyed. The hilltop sites, encircled by ditch and bank in Neolithic times, were generally reoccupied and their defences elaborated in the Iron Age. As yet no Neolithic corn-plots are definitely known, possibly because the same ground continued in use subsequently. It was during the Neolithic Age that Britain received the religion associated with **megalithic** (big stone) **monuments,** some of which, again, are known to have been destroyed in the last few centuries. Long-chambered tombs, or **dolmens,** were probably originally covered with earth. Erection of megaliths continued during the Bronze Age, to which belong many **standing stones**—in single lines or avenues, solitary (**menhirs:** these are, however, difficult to date) or in circles (**cromlechs**). A highly organized society is implied. The rarity or absence of fortified sites of this period is taken by archaeologists to signify a long period of peace. The greatest megalithic monuments of all, such as Avebury and Stonehenge, are similar to the great cathedrals of to-day, in that they were altered and added to during a lengthy use and cannot be ascribed to a single period.

Bronze Age Antiquities

The Bronze Age in Britain was introduced by numerous immigrants, whose period of dominance roughly coincided with the sub-Boreal climatic phase, when the climate was drier than it now is, and the summers were warmer. A number of authorities hold that a lower water-table encouraged pasture rather than tillage on the downlands, and suggest that man tended to live near the springlines, that is, in the valleys. It is important to bear this point in mind in considering the **round barrows** of certain uplands. Excavation has shown that where round barrows are numerous they usually belong, as a group, to the Bronze Age, although secondary burials—of later date but in the same barrows—are not uncommon. The geographer taking a synoptic view may expect to find round barrows concentrated on the higher ground, often in precisely those parts where the long Neolithic barrows occur, and may justifiably infer that in the Bronze Age, as in earlier times, the permeable uplands were the most favourable tracts; but he should think in terms of hilltop pasture, remembering that although the barrows prove exploitation of the land, they are burial-places and not dwelling-sites. It is on some *impermeable* uplands, Dartmoor, for example, that Bronze Age houses and villages are coming to be known on the plateau top, together with walled cattle enclosures such as Grimspound, near Moreton Hampstead. The settlement of Dartmoor is itself a measure of the climatic difference between Bronze Age and present times.

The Early Iron Age

In about 750 B.C., at approximately the time that a more oceanic climate was re-established in the sub-Atlantic Phase, the Celtic invasions began. The earlier arrivals were of Bronze Age culture, but iron implements became dominant from about 500 B.C. onwards. The heavier rainfall and higher water-table allowed tillage to spread widely over the downlands, but promoted peat growth on the impermeable rocks of many highland tracts. Doubtless much evidence of Bronze Age occupance is buried under sub-Atlantic peat, while many Neolithic plots must have been obliterated by Celtic ploughing. For about seven centuries after the first invasions, the plough used was the light Mediterranean form, which did not turn the sod and was well adapted to the shallow upland soils. Cross-ploughing of small, roughly rectangular patches gave rise to the characteristic pattern of **Celtic Fields.** Adjacent plots are separated by low banks or **lynchets,**[1] originally faced with stone, where earth accumulated at the downhill side of individual plots. "Scratch agriculture" of this kind put a great deal of the Chalk uplands under tillage, and is also known, for instance, from the outcrops of Carboniferous Limestone, where natural drainage was also good and the soil light and shallow. It was associated with a shift of habitation back to the higher ground, as occasionally shown on the O.S. map by the notation "British Village" (now being discontinued). This upland cultivation seems to have continued into, and possibly throughout, the Roman occupation, while according to Childe the "Celtic Fields" of Highland Britain were still cultivated in the Middle Ages or later.

The Celtic influx ended the lengthy peace of the Bronze Age, replacing it by militarism, raids, and war. The unsettled conditions are reflected by the many fortified hilltop sites—usually called "camps"

---

[1] See also p. 157.

on O.S. maps—which, as already stated, include some formerly occupied in Neolithic times. Authorities differ on whether these strong-points were permanently inhabited or were merely refuges for men and livestock in time of danger, but, whatever the fact, their existence points to a time of much disorder. Where they occur, the map interpreter should note their siting, wherein marked tactical as well as strategic advantages are often apparent. In Scotland these strongholds include vitrified forts, usually so named on the map. The original walls included substantial timbers, which when fired caused a partial fusion of the stones.

By about 100 B.C. a widening political grouping had caused many hill forts to be abandoned. Defended cities were becoming established on the lower ground. The downhill shift, although still slight, was emphasized from about 75 B.C. onwards, when Belgic invaders introduced the heavy plough, an implement fitted with wheel and coulter and capable of working the claylands. It is precisely because the two forms of plough are suited to contrasted soils that the Celtic field patterns remain visible to-day, for the heavy Belgic model, which was used to turn the land in long strips, would have obliterated the outlines of the squarish plots.

Roman Sites

Clearance of the damp, low-lying areas was at first slow, and is known to have been effected mostly in post-Roman times. In this connection the sites of Roman towns are less significant than the sites of villas, which were largely self-contained and self-sufficient agricultural establishments. They lie almost exclusively outside those belts which are, in the natural state, badly drained; but the Roman period is recorded most distinctively in features of civil and military occupation, superimposed on the terrain rather than adapted to it. However strikingly the Roman roads avoid or circumvent major obstacles, and however strategically placed the camps, forts, and towns, the patterns remain geometrical, corresponding with the texture of the country only in the broadest manner.

Earthworks of the Dark Ages

The withdrawal of the legions in about A.D. 450 re-opened the country to active immigration. Anglo-Saxon and Scandinavian penetration and settlement have been discussed in another chapter. Here it remains to mention only linear earthworks, often named "dyke" or "ditch," of which many belong to the Dark Ages. Although some may have been constructed in haste for immediate tactical purposes, others had strategic or political value, delimiting a frontier or the boundary of a domain. Geographically a number are of great interest, in that they stop short at the edge of low clayland, whence it is inferred that, when the works were constructed, the clay was still wooded and not easily penetrable.

Towards the west of the country many earthworks, linear earthworks in particular, bear names reminiscent of the Arthurian legends; towards the east they are more commonly credited to the Danes or to Grim, the Devil. In most cases the implied dating or origin is wildly inaccurate and should on no account be accepted.

Lynchets

The one class of earthwork not yet reviewed in its entirety is the lynchet. The term is applied to at least three distinct forms of different date. The narrow, striplike, near-horizontal terraces of steep slopes (for example, on the scarped edge of Salisbury Plain near Mere) are usually taken as cultivation-terraces of unknown date. On O.S. maps at 1/63,360 and 1/25,000 there is room only for single rows of hachures, which have to stand for whole systems of lynchets. The low banks which bound Celtic fields are not always indicated on the 1-in. map, if the name is inserted; elsewhere hachures are again used. In the Yorkshire Dales a third type of lynchet occurs, this time on the lower slopes and on parts of the valley bottoms. Like the first type, it consists of a narrow flat strip terminating in a steep descent on the downhill side, but although some groups run across the slope others run almost directly down. It has been urged that these lynchets are of Anglian date.

It is hoped that this brief review, summarized in the Table on page 158, will be of use in the interpretation of prehistoric occupance. Deficient though it may be, the map record is capable of revealing something of the former relationship of man to ground, and of showing that in earlier times, even more markedly than to-day, the qualities of the setting were not without influence on man's activity.

Interpretation from an O.S. Map

The principles stated above will now be applied in a specific interpretation. The map selected is O.S. 1/63,360 (Seventh Series) Sheet 165 (Weston-super-Mare), on which physical distributions have already

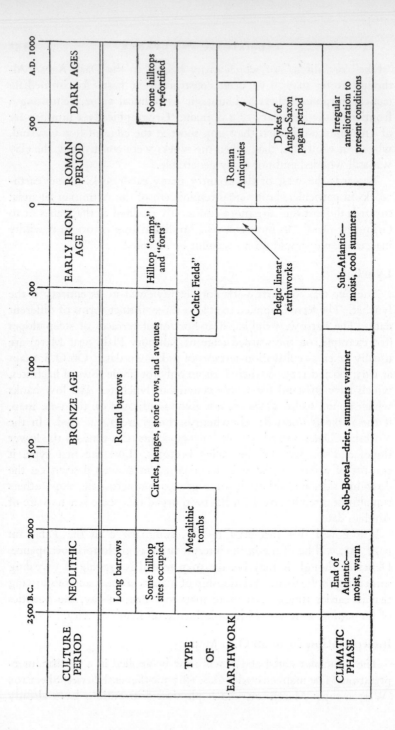

CULTURE PERIOD	NEOLITHIC	BRONZE AGE	EARLY IRON AGE	ROMAN PERIOD	DARK AGES
					Some hilltops re-fortified
	Long barrows	Round barrows			
	Some hilltop sites occupied	Circles, henges, stone rows, and avenues	Hilltop "camps" and "forts"	Roman Antiquities	
TYPE OF EARTHWORK	Megalithic tombs	"Celtic Fields"		Dykes of Anglo-Saxon pagan period	
			Belgic linear earthworks		
CLIMATIC PHASE	End of Atlantic—moist, warm	Sub-Boreal—drier, summers warmer	Sub-Atlantic—moist, cool summers	Irregular amelioration to present conditions	

Scale: 2500 B.C. — 2000 — 1500 — 1000 — 500 — 0 — 500 — 1000 A.D.

been studied in Chapter X. Certain morphological boundaries relevant to the present aim have been added, in Fig. 10, to a map of

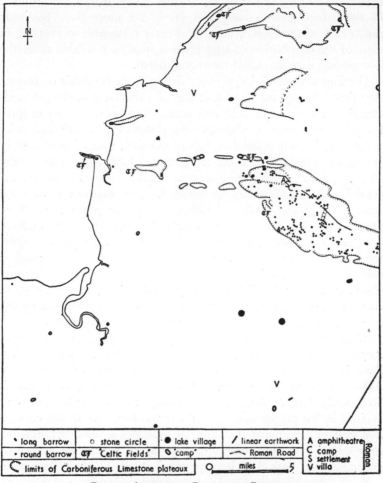

• long barrow	○ stone circle	● lake village	/ linear earthwork	A amphitheatre
• round barrow	₢ᵮ 'Celtic Fields'	◗ 'camp'	⌒ Roman Road	C camp
				S settlement
⊂ limits of Carboniferous Limestone plateaux		O ——— miles ——— 5		V villa

FIG. 10. ANALYSIS OF PREHISTORIC EVIDENCE
Early antiquities as shown on O.S. Seventh Series 1/63,360, Sheet 165, with the addition of two lake villages
Crown Copyright reserved

earthworks taken from the O.S. sheet. The close general relation between the form of the ground and the distribution of remains is immediately obvious: it is emphasized by a detailed inspection.

The eight long barrows are assumed to be probably Neolithic.

Five occur on the Mendip plateau, three on the dissected scarpland to the north. All are prominently sited, either on summits or on **false crests,** where they appear on the skyline as seen from lower ground. In themselves these burial-places prove no more than Neolithic penetration of the upland, but it is entirely reasonable to suppose, in view of the distribution of later features, that in Neolithic times the low ground was untouched forest and marsh.

The four aligned circles, possibly dating from Neolithic or Bronze Age times, suggest the ritual practices of a relatively stable and well-organized society. The abundant round barrows show that in (presumably) the Bronze Age, the Mendip plateau was broadly and easily penetrable, i.e. not more than lightly wooded, if not indeed widely grazed and tilled. Of a total of 145 round barrows, 137 lie on the Mendips, nearly all on the flat summit-plane where, however, the gentle north-easterly slopes are avoided. Two barrows lie near the summit of Bleadon Hill, a detached portion of plateau, and three more in the dissected northern scarpland where long barrows have been previously noted, giving a total of 142 on high ground. Of the remaining three, that at 2045 (marked "tumulus" on the map) is exceptionally placed very close to the fen. Walborough (3157) and Castle Batch (3663), each on low ground a little above the 50-ft. contour, may not be tumuli at all, although they are marked by the hachure symbol, for the names suggest a post-Roman origin.

Whatever reservations are necessary on the grounds that not all round barrows have survived, or have been located and mapped, there is very good evidence of selective occupance of the uplands. Although, as remarked above, barrows are not dwelling-sites, there is little doubt that the damper valley bottoms as well as the fen were avoided by the people who made the round barrows. In this connection it should be noted that there is little dry ground between the steep edges of the limestone uplands and the bottom lands, so that grazing at least must have been practised chiefly on the plateau-tops.

Where summits are so wide and flat it is pointless to look for an alignment of barrows along a ridge-top, such as may be found in other parts of the country. The Mendip plateau offers negligible obstacles to circulation, providing a belt rather than a line of hilltop between the forests and marshes on either side.

The probable Iron Age antiquities recorded on Sheet 165 and in Fig. 10 include twenty-four specified "camps" or large circular earthworks. As a group the "camps" are remarkably well sited, occupying steep-sided single hills or prominent spurs, invariably commanding a wide range of country. As far as may be judged from the mapped distributions, this area was more deeply penetrated in the Iron Age than in earlier times, for defensive works appear on the coastal hills where no barrows are shown, and "Celtic Fields," in so far as they belong to the Iron Age, prove cultivation in that period of hilltops beyond the mapped extent of round barrows. As noted previously, the "Celtic Fields" should be regarded more as relics of an agricultural system than as the trace of a particular people, but when they and the "camps" are considered together it seems justifiable to conclude that during the Iron Age the upland stows were still the most attractive.

The O.S. map omits two Iron Age village sites, at Meare and Glastonbury respectively, which have been marked in Fig. 10. The omission is a serious one, for the sites are those of two very well-known marsh villages, which exemplify the beginnings of lowland occupance in Iron Age times. Their absence from the map, corresponding to an extremely faint trace on the ground, is a fact that illustrates the need for caution in treating negative evidence.

The three Roman villas marked signify civil occupation. They lie severally near the crest of the Poldens (4824), on the southern side of Banwell Hill (3958) and alongside the embanked and tidal Yeo (4065). This last site is unusual for a villa, but its natural drainage may have been better in Roman times than it is now. A lowland coast of this type is capable of changing considerably in two thousand years. No recognizable trace remains of any roads which may have linked the villas with the national road system, which is here represented by part of the Fosse Way in the south-east and by portions and traces of Roman roads on the Mendips. The paved ways on the plateau served a Settlement and a Camp, with an associated Amphitheatre near Charterhouse on Mendip (4955)—evidently a civil as well as a military establishment existed here. This map fails to suggest that the Roman settlement was connected with lead mining, although it is well known that this was so. The modern mine buildings, disused but still extant, have also been omitted, the only sign of mining being the three pools impounded by spoil in the spinney at the head of Velvet Bottom.

Among the linear earthworks, some of which are likely to belong to the Dark Ages, New Ditch (5033) is significantly named and strikingly placed. It lies precisely where the crest of the Polden cuesta narrows sharply westwards. It may be wondered if the Old Ditch recorded in a settlement-name near Wells (5049) is an earlier defensive work of the same people. "Intrenchments" above Clevedon on Castle Hill are rather indistinctly shown, and should possibly be associated with the systems of hill-forts on the two ridges enclosing Walton Moor. In any event they mark a site of great tactical, if not strategic, value. Finally, the "earthworks" inland of Weston-super-Mare include some kind of mound as well as a ditch, and occupy a small rise which commands the shortest way across the fen between the Mendips and Worlebury Hill.

It has now been briefly demonstrated that an analytical treatment of the distribution of early antiquities can reveal something of the conquest of the land in prehistoric times, and of the profound changes which have occurred in man's relationship to the geographical setting. Thus, despite the inherent defects of work with partial evidence, a certain limited success may be claimed.

NOTES AND REFERENCES

Eminently readable, but at the same time authoritative, general accounts of prehistoric times in Britain are—

GRAHAME CLARK. *Prehistoric England.* Batsford, London, 1945.

V. GORDON CHILDE. *Prehistoric Communities of the British Isles.* Chambers, Edinburgh, 1940.

SIR CYRIL FOX. *The Personality of Britain.* Fourth Edition. National Museum of Wales, Cardiff, 1943.

JACQUETTA and CHRISTOPHER HAWKES. *Prehistoric Britain.* Chatto and Windus, London, 1949.

STUART PIGGOTT. *British Prehistory.* University Press, Oxford, 1949.

S. E. WINBOLT. *Britain B.C.* Penguin Books, Harmondsworth (Middx.), 1943.

Life in Roman Britain is surveyed by—

R. G. COLLINGWOOD. *Roman Britain.* University Press, Oxford, 1942.

The summary Table given in the text is based chiefly on the works, cited above, of SIR C. FOX and J. and C. HAWKES, together with the following very useful booklet—

ORDNANCE SURVEY. *Field Archaeology, Some Notes for Beginners Issued by the Ordnance Survey.* O.S., Professional Papers, New Series, No. 13, H.M.S.O., 1951.

The question of natural vegetation in early times is broadly reviewed in Fox, op. cit., p. 53 ff.

Post-Roman clearing of woodland is discussed by—

H. C. DARBY. "The Clearing of the English Woodlands." *Geography*, xxxvi, 1951, p. 71.

An accessible account of the Gaulish method of constructing forts with stone and timber, relevant to the problem of vitrified forts, may be obtained from—

CAESAR. *The Conquest of Gaul.* Translated by S. A. HANDFORD. Penguin Books, Harmondsworth, (Middx.), 1951.

Short descriptions of the two marsh villages in Somerset may be found in the books by CLARK and CHILDE referred to above; but, for an instructive comparison between the results obtainable from map interpretation and those yielded by field archaeology, see—

D. P. DOBSON. *Somerset (County Archaeologies Series).* Methuen, London, 1931. (This account bears out the interpretation given here, but supplements it considerably in some respects, for example, by recording finds of implements, and more Roman villas than are shown by the O.S. 1/63,360 sheet (cf. Fig. 10, p. 159, and Dobson's map, pp. 132–3). Dobson also analyses the Saxon finds.)

The study of archaeological distributions generally is greatly assisted by reference to the maps in FOX, op. cit. (p. 162), and to the special maps of the Ordnance Survey; for example, Map of Roman Britain, Map of Neolithic Wessex, Map of Monastic Britain, etc., which can be obtained in annotated form.

PART III

SPECIAL TOPICS

CHAPTER XV

MORPHOMETRIC ANALYSIS

We require the permeating accuracy of scientific methods as well as knowledge of basal scientific facts.—FAIRGRIEVE

MORPHOMETRY is the measurement of shape. Morphometric analysis of maps is intended to reveal and define, more clearly and precisely than can be done by unaided inspection, the general form of the ground as represented on the map. The techniques employed vary in difficulty. Some involve laborious measurement and a certain amount of calculation, but others are rapid, graphic, and simple. All attain a degree of exactitude which is impossible in map reading.

There can, of course, be no substitute for detailed field-work in the study of landform. Very many features of the highest significance appear only on those maps drawn by the field geomorphologist; but the techniques of morphometry are of great use in the rapid exploratory treatment of large areas, in helping the map interpreter to reduce the forms of diversified country to some kind of order, and in the treatment of certain classes of data which are not well derived from field study.

For convenience' sake, the methods reviewed in the following paragraphs are grouped under the four somewhat arbitrary heads of geometric, arithmetic, volumetric, and clinometric analysis, according to whether the landscape element measured is the general form of the ground, the relation of area to height, the volume of specific features, or the degree of slope. The first group comprises most of the rapid methods of analysis that the interpreter might expect to find useful in a first approach to a given problem: some of these should undoubtedly be standard practice. The remainder, requiring more time and lengthier measurement, are certain to be less generally applied. They are included here, not so much in order to provide additional tools for frequent use, as to demonstrate the considerable possibilities of this kind of work, and to explain the construction of various kinds of diagram which are coming to be widely used in descriptive accounts.

1. Geometric Analysis

Work of this kind is designed to simplify the relief distributions of the contour map, and to reveal the major landform patterns of the

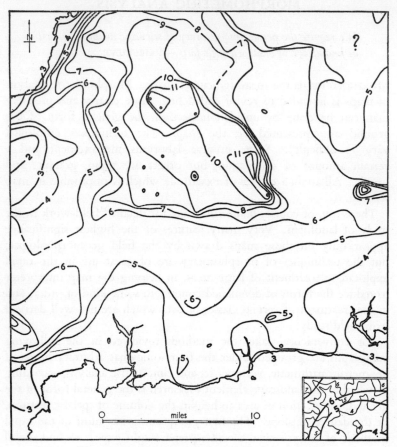

FIG. 11. GENERALIZED CONTOURS, FOR THE AREA SHOWN ON SHEET 186
OF THE O.S. SEVENTH SERIES 1/63,360 MAP
Inset, method of constructing generalized contours
(Based on the O.S. map, by permission)

area treated. The simplest exercise, and the most widely useful, is the construction of **generalized contours,** which touch the actual contours at the tips of spurs but are carried across existing valleys (see Fig. 11). The surface defined by generalized contours is that which would be observed if the valleys were filled in to the general level of the inter-fluves. If the crests of divides are remnants of a platform, whether erosional or structural, its form is approximately reconstructed in the generalized contours. When platforms demonstrated in this manner truncate structures they must be erosional.

It is often found that in a given highland tract the major forms of the ground, however greatly diversified by present dissection, consist in broad flats or very gentle slopes, separated by much steeper slopes or topographic risers. The flats may be miles wide, the risers tens or hundreds of feet high: the whole constitutes an impressive physio-graphic stairway. Generalized contours are eminently suited to reveal such major forms: they lie far apart on the flats and bunch together at the risers, as shown in Fig. 11, where they are drawn for the area of the O.S. 1/63,360 (Seventh Series) Sheet 186. It has already been seen in Chapter V that this landscape can be interpreted in terms of denudation controlled by a sequence of higher base-levels: con-clusions drawn from inspection of the map are amplified as well as confirmed by generalized contours. The residual hills above the wide plateau of Bodmin Moor are encircled by the generalized 1,100-ft. contours; the plateau itself extends to the 900-ft. line on the eastern side and to the 800-ft. on the west; the steep edge is well brought out in close spacing, which also marks the possible old cliff line inland of Tintagel. In this general view there is a very marked topographic break between the bounding slope of the granite boss and the broad flat of the lower ground. Both on the east and on the south this break occurs between 600 and 700 ft. O.D. Note also the similar break of general slope, at a similar height, on the north-eastern side of Hens-barrow. If more detailed work—for example, on the 1/25,000 map, but primarily in the field—proved that the change from slope to flat was nearly horizontal, one would suspect the presence of an old shore-line, related to a base-level higher than, but parallel to, the present one. This would imply that the fall of base-level was not, in this area, accompanied by tilting, in which case any old shorelines at lower altitudes should also remain horizontal: now the run of the generalized contour at 400 ft. O.D. in the basins of the Looe and Fowey is not inconsistent with a former shoreline at about this level, such as has already been suggested by a study of the north coast.

Serial profiles are drawn along equally spaced parallel lines, which run in the direction of general slope, if any. When closely spaced enough, such profiles may indicate or suggest the presence of erosional or structural platforms. If geological detail be added, they illustrate the relation between structure and relief.

As serial profiles are not easily compared with one another at a glance, especially if the series is large, **superimposed** and **projected profiles** have been devised for the purpose of rapid comparison. In a superimposed profile the entire series of profiles is plotted in a single diagram. If any platforms exist, of whatever nature, they are likely to be reflected in the grouping of lines (Fig. 12a), whereas topographic risers are distributed over the whole figure; but the superimposition of many lines may result in a confused diagram. Hence the practice

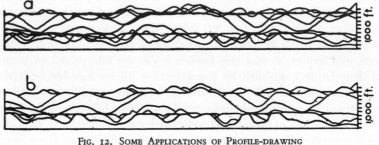

FIG. 12. SOME APPLICATIONS OF PROFILE-DRAWING
(a) Superimposed profiles.
(b) The same profiles projected.
Signs of planation appear at 400 and at 900 ft.

of simplifying, in the projected profile. Here the first of the series of profiles, as it were the nearest to the observer, is drawn complete; the second, or next nearest, only where it rises above the second; and so on throughout the series. Thus a kind of panoramic sketch (without perspective) is obtained, which reveals accordance of level at specific altitudes (Fig. 12b). Care is needed in laying out the lines of profile, for if a great deal of high ground occurs in the earlier profiles the later may be heavily obscured. Some detail must in any event be lost, for simplicity is achieved only by means of sacrificing part of the data.

Profiles drawn along arbitrary lines are likely to miss significant breaks of slope. Hence the use of **spur-top profiles,** drawn along the axes of interfluves. It is doubtful, however, if these have any advantage over generalized contours, for the breaks of slope which they are designed to reveal are precisely those by which the spacing of generalized contours is governed. Needless to say, the matter is different with spur-top profiles surveyed on the ground, whereby certain features of the terrain may be fittingly sampled.

Serial cross-profiles of valleys can bring to light the valley-in-valley forms produced by rejuvenation, if these forms should be present and sufficiently well marked to be recorded on the map. It has been suggested that, where former cross-profiles can be reconstructed, they may provide a basis for reconstructing former long-profiles also, but in the writer's opinion their value in this connection is not great.

One of the chief aims in constructing the **long-profiles of rivers** is to discover any irregularities that may exist. If a river has been rejuvenated, as for example by a rapid fall of base-level, it is often found that the surviving portion of the earlier profile meets the developing newer profile in a **knickpoint** of characteristic form. On general grounds one should expect very many rivers to display composite profiles, which like polycyclic landscapes are the product of more than one erosion-cycle; but not every break of profile is a knickpoint of cyclic origin: it is one thing to determine the profile form, another to interpret it. If base-level falls, the headward wave of rejuvenation works its way up all the stream systems affected, so that a knickpoint on one trunk stream should be associated with knickpoints on other trunk streams and also on tributaries. A synoptic plot of the profiles of a single-stream system, or of a group of trunk streams, should bring to light any general correspondence of form. In practice, however, complications are introduced, for example, by differences of rock resistance, gaps in the record, the peculiarities of individual streams and the diversity of actual sequences of rejuvenation. Thus, even when long-profiles have been constructed by the only reliable and satisfactory method, detailed levelling of the ground, the task of interpretation is difficult. A map interpreter must rely on contours, not all of which may have been instrumentally surveyed, and must reconcile himself to the fact that long-profiles constructed from maps are certain to omit many significant details of form. The interval between instrumental contours on the O.S. 1/63,360 series is too wide for any but the coarsest work. Consequently any long-profiles drawn therefrom are to be read with extreme caution, except perhaps where the river gradient is generally steep and breaks of profile are very well marked. Extrapolation of parts of a composite profile, so as to link them with former base-levels, should not be lightly undertaken. Research proves the futility of supposing that surviving profile curves can be accurately extended in this manner. The interpreter should therefore confine himself to suggesting, where the evidence is particularly clear, that a certain profile element *may be* related to a former base-level which has been identified by other means, for example, by generalized contours.

For what they are worth, a number of long-profiles plotted from Sheet 186 of the O.S. 1/63,360 (Seventh Series) are given in Fig. 13, where marked breaks of gradient appear.

A further method which relies on the cartographic record of stream gradients, and which is therefore to be employed with reservation, is that of mapping the **migrational tendencies of divides.** It is assumed that, other things being equal, a stream with a steeper gradient will extend its catchment headward more rapidly than one with a gentler.

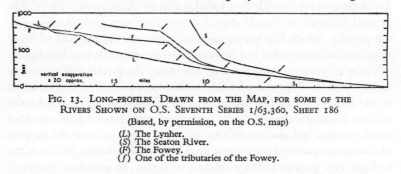

FIG. 13. LONG-PROFILES, DRAWN FROM THE MAP, FOR SOME OF THE
RIVERS SHOWN ON O.S. SEVENTH SERIES 1/63,360, SHEET 186
(Based, by permission, on the O.S. map)
(*L*) The Lynher.
(*S*) The Seaton River.
(*F*) The Fowey.
(*f*) One of the tributaries of the Fowey.

By comparing the gradients of opposing streams on either side of a divide, where fortunately for the purpose in hand the gradients are likely to be steep and streams much of a size, one may discover where the advantage lies, and map the apparent direction of divide movement as toward the streams with gentler gradients. Since relative gradient is not the only factor which ought to be considered, the result obtained is subject to some inaccuracy; but it has been found to work well in practice, and to be capable of showing which streams tend to enlarge their catchments at the expense of which neighbours.

2. Arithmetic Analysis

Under this head will be noted analytical techniques which employ numerical values, whether of height alone or of height-plus-area. Mathematically speaking, the simplest item is the **summit-plane,** which is commonly indicated or suggested by a close similarity of summit heights in a given area. If the accordant summits are numerous, broad, and flat-topped, they may be looked on as the remnants of a once extensive platform, which, if it truncates reconstructed folds, faults, and rock formations, must have been the product of erosion; but, where the summits are peaks, as in a great deal of glaciated highland, the problem is more difficult. One usually finds that, although the summits are roughly accordant in height, any reconstructed summit-"plane" must be irregular in form and of considerable relief. Here is the real difficulty: by no means all former cycles of erosion approached completion, so that some former landscapes, if accurately reconstructed, would appear hilly or even mountainous. Unless the evidence is abundant and satisfactory, the interpreter can do no more than point out a general similarity of summit heights.

Where a great many points have been levelled, their frequency may be plotted against altitude. They are grouped within selected ranges of height, for example, 0–99 ft., 100–199 ft., and plotted on a graph, the **altimetric-frequency curve.** A number of such curves have been constructed for parts of England by Hollingworth, who employed a wealth of unpublished O.S. data, and for parts of France by Baulig, who showed thereby the possibilities of morphometric work with hachured maps. The method of treatment is purely statistical, being designed to show at which altitudes there are relatively large frequencies of levelled points. When large areas are treated, and when more than one area gives high frequencies at corresponding heights, it becomes possible that the high frequencies relate to erosional platforms referable to former high base-levels.

The assumption made is that remnants of platforms, in dissected country, lie on hilltops whose heights are determined in the course of survey. A similar assumption is made in plotting the frequency of closed contours. In the area selected for treatment, all contours closed round outlying hills or spur-tops are identified, and the totals plotted against height as in the altimetric-frequency curve. As before, the diagram may be expected to reveal something of the general form of the ground, and of the presence of any platforms.

Planimetric data may be similarly treated. Areas between successive contours are measured, most rapidly and satisfactorily by the planimeter itself.[1] When the total area between each pair of contours is plotted against height, in the same way as for the altimetric-frequency curve, the resulting figure is the **height-frequency curve** (to give it a distinctive name) whereby the general form of the ground is well summarized. If the several areas between pairs of contours are

---

[1] None of the other means of measurement seems in any way preferable to the use of this effective instrument.

expressed as percentages of the total area measured, the familiar **hypso-metric** (or hypsographic) **curve** is produced. Major topographic breaks can appear on this curve although less clearly than on the height-frequency curve which is far more sensitive to small differences of area. Moreover, the hypsometric curve gives a misleading im-pression of the form of the ground at the highest levels, for which reason the **clinographic** (or hypsographoid) **curve** has been pro-posed as an alternative. Here the total area above a given contour is regarded as a circle, and the distance between the y-axis of the graph and the point plotted against that contour is proportional to the radius of the circle. A clinographic curve drawn with true vertical scale would show the true mean slope between successive contours.

These several forms of altimetric- and height-frequency curve are illustrated in Fig. 14.

Relative relief, the vertical distance between the tops of divides and the bottoms of valleys, may be readily determined from maps. The map is gridded, the difference of height between the highest and lowest points in each square is plotted, and the values obtained are used to construct an isopleth map of relative relief. Such a map is obviously capable of expressing, in numerical terms, a significant element of landscape texture.

3. Volumetric Analysis

The expression of relative relief by the method just outlined un-fortunately takes little account of the form of divides, apart from their height. It is easy to imagine two contrasted lansdcapes with identical relative relief, one with narrow valleys deeply cut between broad, flat-topped interfluves, the other with wide, flat-bottomed valleys separated by narrow, but still high, residual divides; but the greater the bulk of rock contained in the divides, the heavier the task of denudation still to be performed. The volume of divides may be allowed for by calculating the **mean available relief.** Available relief is zero on a surface passed through the bottoms of the large valleys—the *streamline surface*, which is defined by generalized contours linking points where the larger rivers cross actual contours. Now if this surface is planimetered, one may easily calculate the volume of rock between it and base-level. Similarly, the actual surface is planimetered and a similar calculation made. The difference between the two volumes gives the total volume of the divides, which if divided

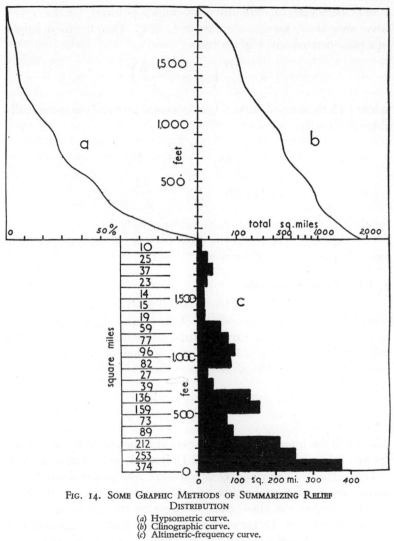

FIG. 14. SOME GRAPHIC METHODS OF SUMMARIZING RELIEF
DISTRIBUTION

(a) Hypsometric curve.
(b) Clinographic curve.
(c) Altimetric-frequency curve.

All curves are drawn from the figures given at the bottom left

by the area treated gives the mean height of divide over the whole area, i.e. the mean available relief.

In practice a certain economy of working is possible. Let the cumulative areas above specific contours be l_o, l_1, l_n. Then the mean height of a planimetered area is given by—

$$h = \frac{VI}{l_n} \left(\sum l - \frac{l_o + l_n}{2} \right)$$

where VI is the vertical interval between contours; and the mean available relief is given by—

$$r = \frac{VI}{l_n} (M_a - M_s)$$

where $$M_a, M_s = \sum l - \frac{l_o + l_n}{2}$$

for the actual and streamline surfaces respectively.

The first equation is also suitable for use in determining, for example, the volumes of reservoirs.

4. Clinometric Analysis

None of the techniques so far described gives a quantitative indication of the roughness or smoothness of the terrain. A rapid and simple method of calculating the **mean slope,** regardless of direction, is as follows: the map is gridded and the number of points at which contours cross the grid lines is counted; the tangent of the mean slope is given by—

$$\frac{n}{G} \times \frac{VI}{3661}$$

where n is the number of grid/contour crossings, G is the aggregate length of the grid lines in miles, and VI is the contour interval in feet.

The techniques outlined may be varied or extended in a number of ways, which will not however be described here. Enough has been said to illustrate the chief ways of handling the cartographic data embodied in a map. Of the methods listed, the drawing of generalized contours and of projected profiles, and the calculation of mean slope can be recommended as rapid in practice and highly informative in result. They are, in addition, suitable for use with most contoured maps. As they do not require laborious measurement or computation, they might well be chosen as the first methods of analysing physical distributions, with the reservation that generalized contours may be difficult to construct for areas of glaciated highland.

NOTES AND REFERENCES

The general problem of strand-line movements is discussed by—

H. BAULIG. *The Changing Sea Level.* Institute of British Geographers, Publication No. 3. George Philip, London, 1935.

Some of the types of diagram referred to in this chapter are already sufficiently familiar from standard texts. For full details of the various methods, and for examples of their application, see—

S. W. WOOLDRIDGE and D. L. LINTON. *Structure, Surface, and Drainage in South-East England.* George Philip, London, 1955. (Generalized contours: Figs. 15, 27.)

J. BARRELL. "The Piedmont Terraces of the Appalachians." *Amer. Journ. Science,* xlix, 1920, p. 227. (Projected profiles.)

A. E. TRUEMAN. "Erosion Levels in the Bristol District," etc. *Proc. Bristol Naturalists' Society,* viii, 1938, p. 402. (Superimposed profiles.)

R. F. PEEL. "The North Tyne Valley." *Geogr. Journ.* xcviii, 1941, p. 5. (Serial cross-profiles of valleys.)

G. H. DURY. "Remarks on the Migration of Divides in the Neighbourhood of Northampton." *Journ. Northamptonshire Natural History Society,* xxxi, 1949, p. 115. (Migrational tendencies of divides.)

D. L. LINTON. "Problems of Scottish Scenery." *Scot. Geog. Mag.,* lxvii, 1951, p. 65. (Summit-plane.)

H. BAULIG. "Les Hauts Niveaux d'Érosion Eustatique dans le Bassin de Paris." *Ann. de Géog.,* xxxvii, 1928, pp. 288, 385. (Altimetric-frequency curve.)

S. E. HOLLINGWORTH. "The Recognition and Correlation of High-level Erosion-surfaces in Britain." *Quart. Journ. Geol. Soc.,* xciv, 1938, p. 55. (Altimetric-frequency curve.)

E. ROMER. "Une Nouvelle Représentation Graphique de l'Hypsométrie." *Comptes Rendus, Congrès Internat. de Géographie, Paris,* 1931, Tome I, p. 328. (Clinographic curve.)

J. HANSON-LOWE. "The Clinographic Curve." *Geol. Mag.,* lxxii, 1935, p. 180. (Hypsometric and clinographic curves.)

W. G. V. BALCHIN. *Contributions to the Geomorphology of South-west England.* Ph.D. Thesis, University of London Library, 1950. (Closed contours.)

G. H. SMITH. "The Relative Relief of Ohio." *Geogr. Review,* xxxv, 1935, p. 272. (Relative relief.)

G. H. DURY. "Quantitative Measurement of Available Relief and of Depth of Dissection." *Geol. Mag.*, lxxxviii, 1951, p. 339. (Available relief.)

C. K. WENTWORTH. "A Simplified Method of Determining the Average Slope of Land Surfaces." *Amer. Journ. Science*, Fifth Series, xx, 1930, p. 184. (Slope analysis.)

The following must be included in a list of references to work on long-profiles—

H. BAULIG. The Changing Sea Level. (Above.)

H. BAULIG. "Le Profil d'Équilibre: Histoire et Critique." *Comptes Rendus, Congrès Internat. de Géographie*, Cairo, 1925, Tome III.

H. BAULIG. "The Reconstruction of Stream Profiles." *Journ. Geomorph.*, iii, 1940, p. 3.

V. S. JOVANOVIĆ. *Les Profils Fluviatils en Long, etc.*, Colin, Paris, 1940.

A. AUSTIN MILLER. "Attainable Standards of Accuracy in the Determination of Pre-glacial Sea Levels, etc." *Journ. Geomorph.*, ii, 1939, p. 95.

As an example of the reconstruction of past profiles, one may refer to R. F. PEEL: *The North Tyne Valley* (p. 177). Work with a particular bearing on the area represented on O.S. 1/63,360 (New Popular) Sheet 186, from which Fig. 11 has been drawn, includes—

W. G. V. BALCHIN. "The Erosion Surfaces of North Cornwall." *Geogr. Journ.*, xc, 1937, p. 52.

J. F. N. GREEN. "The Terraces of Southernmost England." *Quart. Journ. Geol. Soc.*, xcii, 1936, p. lviii.

Other references are given at the end of Chapter V.

Papers which, in their several ways, are relevant to the questions raised here are—

G. H. DURY. "Methods of Cartographical Analysis in Geomorphological Research." *Journ. Indian Geogr. Soc.*, Jubilee Volume, 1951.

A. AUSTIN MILLER. *The Dissection and Analysis of Maps*. Institute of British Geographers, Publication No. 14. George Philip, London, 1948, p. 1.

The analysis of aspect, not discussed in the foregoing text, may be studied in—

A. GARNETT. "Isolation, Topography, and Settlement in the Alps." *Geogr. Review*, xxv, 1935, p. 601.

A. GARNETT. *Insolation and Relief*. Institute of British Geographers, Publication No. 5. George Philip, London, 1937.

Panorama construction is described by—

D. SYLVESTER. "A Method of Panorama Construction from Contoured Maps." *Geography*, xxviii, 1943, p. 12.

Block-diagrams are considered at some length in—

A. K. LOBECK. *Block Diagrams*. Wiley, New York, 1924.

A briefer treatment is given in—

C. B. BROWN and F. DEBENHAM. *Structure and Surface, etc.* Edward Arnold, London, 1929. (Chapter XI.)

While the references cited above remain of historical interest, and while they bear directly on the cartographical exercises suggested in the foregoing chapter, neither they nor the above text indicate the nature, aims, and scope of recent developments in morphometry. Among the papers describing modern applications of statistical method are—

A. N. STRAHLER. "Hypsometric (Area-height) Analysis of Erosional Topography," *Bull. Geol. Soc. Amer.*, lxiii, 1952, p. 1117.

A. N. STRAHLER. "Quantitative Slope Analysis," *ibid.*, lxvii, 1958, p. 57.

CHAPTER XVI

CARTOGRAPHICAL APPRECIATION

By H. C. Brookfield, B.A., Ph.D., and
G. H. Dury, M.A., Ph.D., F.G.S.

Lecturers in Geography, Birkbeck College, University of London

In every work regard the writer's end,
For none can compass more than they intend.—Pope

Maps: O.S. 1/63,360 (Seventh Series) Sheet 114 (Boston and Skegness), 1954; O.S. Tourist Map, 1/63,360 (Lorn and Lochaber), 1959; U.S. Geological Survey 1/62,500 (Pinal County (Arizona) Casa Grande Quadrangle), 1925; O.S. 1/25,000, Sheet SO/00, 1948; Germany 1/25,000, Sheet 4506 (Duisburg), 1958; Netherlands 1/25,000, New Series, Sheet 25a (Haarlem), 1952

Cartographical appreciation is the critical assessment of maps. It involves study of cartographical methods and techniques, and estimation of their success or failure in the representation of land. Like regional geography, it can be executed on more than one level, but, also like regional geography, it depends both upon the use of facts and upon subjective judgments. In recent years the subjective element in regional geography has become highly suspect, and strenuous efforts have been made to eliminate it, but the subjective element in cartographical appreciation has suffered merely by neglect.

To identify the forms of notation used on a particular map is simple enough, even if the key to symbols is scanty or absent. To identify the several notations of a number of map-series takes longer, but the drawing of comparisons still requires nothing but moderate pains. When the suitability of notations comes in question, however, judgments have to be passed. Although full agreement on all points of failure, success, and suitability cannot be looked for, critics are likely to pass many verdicts in common, even though the final task of appreciation—the criticism of the map *as a whole*—will inevitably be affected by the taste, experience, and aesthetic susceptibilities of individuals.

The final step is a form of art-criticism. Just as a work of art cannot be described in terms of an analytical list of its parts, so it is not enough merely to analyse the range of information presented on a map, and to identify the scales of notation employed. Art critics can draw on an extensive vocabulary, which has no parallel in the geographical world —fortunately, perhaps, since the vocabulary of art-criticism can suffer from rapid changes of fashion and from injections of pretentiousness. But these very circumstances are little more than responses to a fundamental difficulty, namely, that there are very few common words designed to express what the art critic has to say. A geographer, possibly untrained in aesthetics and long encouraged to view subjectivity with deep suspicion, can be very badly equipped to criticize a whole map.

Cartographical appreciation cannot be learned by rule of thumb. Long practice and considerable patience are both needed. The largely mechanical business of studying representation is so straightforward that it might seem pointless, did it not invariably induce respect for map-makers, reveal the wide range of choice in the designing of maps, and make clear the wide range of actual practice. We strongly urge that this analytical work should be performed with scrupulous care, and that free comparison should be made between different scales of single surveys, different series of single surveys, and maps of different surveys on a single scale. We think it quite justifiable to react favourably or adversely to the first sight of an unfamiliar map, but insist that the initial reaction should be followed both by a study of notation and by an explicit statement of a general assessment.

Maps, like words, have uses rather than meanings. Though the topographical map be the geographer's principal tool, it is made neither by him nor specifically for him. A modern topographical map is a compilation of results obtained by field surveyors, office draughtsmen, archaeologists, local-government surveyors, transport officials, and recording sections of bodies, public and private. In many countries, the original object of a national survey was military, and potential military use still strongly affects the design of maps today. After the military, the next most important class of map-users is perhaps formed by travellers—especially travellers by road. However, it is now common for motorists to use special road maps, one variety of the huge group of special maps which includes Admiralty charts, aeronautical maps, geological maps, land-use maps, soil maps, large-scale plans, and cadastral maps. We are concerned in the present context with none of these. This discussion is limited to the general map, the ordinary topographical map used in most geographical interpretation. Since such a map is a common tool, it is quite unreasonable to expect that it should be designed primarily for geographical purposes. Unless this principle be kept in mind, criticism may be unfair.

The published map must omit a great deal of potential material, and ought to achieve some kind of balance in the material actually represented. Some of the resulting compromises are, by general consent, successful: others are distinct failures. Many map series achieve praiseworthy success with certain classes of information—for instance the representation of height—while failing signally in dealing with others—for instance built-up areas. Again, it is quite possible for individual classes of notation to look clear and handsome in the key, but to fuse together in the map, to combine in a faint array of pale tints, or to constitute an over-vigorous and repellent display of solid, clashing polychrome.

At the outset the critic is liable to take his own national maps as the norm, simply because he is used to them. Adverse criticism is then directed at foreign maps which use unfamiliar systems of notation, or which omit reference to certain kinds of information. As foreign maps become familiar, and as the critic achieves a certain sophistication of cartographical taste, tolerance will grow; but full tolerance is unlikely to be attained without experience of using foreign maps on their own ground. To take an example, the 1/50,000 map of Sweden relies on black hachures and black form-lines for much of its representation of relief, and seems to offer little to the map-reader trained on contours. In fact, however, the techniques employed are admirably suited to the terrain, and it is easy to follow a cross-country route across the terraced drift and glaciated rocky bosses of south-west Sweden with the aid of a standard map.

This is merely one of innumerable examples of the variation of cartographic need from country to country. On the negative side, a given survey will never need to consider the mapping and representation of some classes of feature: symbols for ricefields or vineyards are not required by the Ordnance Survey of Great Britain. On the positive side, features which could be represented on the finished map may vary in apparent significance from country to country, so that there is variety in the care, frequency, and prominence with which particular classes of item are shown. It is to be expected that watercourses of all kinds will be indicated on maps of Holland and Belgium, where they are sub-classified far more elaborately than on British maps of comparable scales. In this general connexion, the critic can usefully note which classes of feature seem to be given special attention, although he cannot go so far as to reconstruct the decisions on policy taken by the map-designers. Furthermore, it is often possible to comment constructively on the treatment of features which are always included—buildings, relief, and lines of communication among them—and to identify accomplishment or deficiency.

Numbers of surveys have traditions of their own. They have developed highly characteristic styles, which enable their products to be identified at once. Several factors contribute to the development, and to the change, of style. Style is affected by the inspiration or competence of heads of surveys, by technical developments in methods of surveying and in methods of printing, and by the financial strength of the survey organization. At any time, the current style usually represents an evolved form of styles formerly used, as can readily be seen from the changing practice of the Ordnance Survey. Wholesale changes are rare; it is quite common to find ancient and modern techniques used together on current maps. Thus, on the O.S. Tourist Map (1/63,360) (Lorn and Lochaber), relief is shown by contours, rock-drawing, partial layer tinting, and a modernized kind of oblique illumination, but the woods, orchards, rough pasture, quarries, and sandhills are marked by symbols which would not have been out-of-place on the maps of private surveyors in the late eighteenth century.

Although many modern surveys use numerous common techniques, there is no reason to suppose that map styles will so converge as to become identical. So long as the perfect map remains unmade, so long as there is no agreement on cartographical perfection, and so long as improvements in printing-processes continue, styles of cartography will persist. The way in which technical improvements occasion changes, and the way in which problems of representation encourage experiment, are well exemplified by the changes introduced by the Ordnance Survey in the quarter-inch series. Sheet 10 (North Wales and Lancashire) of the new 1/250,000 Series, published in 1957, owes much to the true quarter-inch map which it superseded (1/253,440 Map, Sheet 4, North Wales and Manchester, published in 1935). But the style of the Wales and Manchester Special Sheet of the 1/250,000

Map, published in 1959, strongly resembles the style of the current Tourist sheets on 1/63,360. All four maps, however, are recognizable as products of the Ordnance Survey.

Map style can vary sharply from country to country. In view of the mixed emotions aroused by references to nationality, nationalism, and national character, we wish to state firmly that national styles of cartography are just as likely to develop as are styles of book-publication, cartoon-drawing, or poster-painting. A possible influence here is that cartographic style within a country will be affected by the style of the government's maps, so that people come to expect the kind of map provided by the national survey. If so, nationals of a country may well be far easier with their national maps than are geographers who come to the maps as foreigners. Growing familiarity with style will remove difficulties of map-reading, but can do nothing to help the critic in assessing the impalpable quality now in question. To our hopes that the examples of appreciation given later in this chapter will be of assistance, we link a plea for common sense; some maps are certainly too skimpy, others are just as certainly overloaded, but is it not rational to complain that a map is already congested and at the same time to deplore numerous omissions.

Scale

The scale of the map is the most important factor in determining the amount of detail that may be shown and the order of accuracy that can be attained. Topographical scales have been variously defined, but between 1/20,000 and 1/80,000 may be taken as limits for most purposes, while about 1/50,000 is the optimum. Within these limits of scale a map can show all the larger, essential features of the landscape such as may be seen by a walker, including all buildings, and every road and track. The larger the scale, the greater the amount of detail that may be represented, at the expense however of a larger coverage, and also of that wider and more synoptic view of the major features of the countryside which can be gained from smaller-scale maps. For example, in embarking on the morphological division of an area the size of an English county (see Chapter II), it would be unwise to attempt the preliminary division into sections with a map on a scale greater than 1/125,000. As subdivision proceeds, however, larger- and larger-scale maps need to be employed, until for the final subdivision into stows a map on about 1/50,000 and preferably on 1/25,000 is required.

Within general range of topographical scales, there are four chief scales in common use—

1. 1/25,000, long used by Surveys on the Continent, notably the German, and recently adopted by the Ordnance Survey. This scale was found to be of particular use during the recent war, when it was widely employed.

2. 1/50,000, used by several Continental Surveys as the standard topographical scale.

3. 1/62,500, an approximate 1-in. mile scale employed by the U.S. Geological Survey. This scale has the advantage of being a factor of 1,000,000, the series running 1/62,500, 1/125, 000, 1/250,000, 1/500,000, 1/1,000,000.

4. 1/63,360, the exact 1-in. mile scale employed by the Ordnance Survey and most Commonwealth Surveys.

The latter is, perhaps, a rather small scale for topographical maps in so closely settled a country as Great Britain, and the somewhat larger 1/50,000 scale would make for less crowding on maps of densely settled areas.

Maps on these scales deserve close study and comparison. A useful exercise is to examine the same piece of country as represented on maps of different scales. By this means, the oft-repeated question on the "limitations of scale" can best be approached. The problem of the limitations of scale has its mechanical aspects, which are beyond the scope of this chapter, but is also directly relevant to the subject of cartographical appreciation. Detail such as field boundaries and full land-use information is quite appropriate on a scale of 1/25,000 but can heavily overcrowd a topographical map on a smaller scale. Full land-use information is nowhere attempted on O.S. topographical maps, but appears on many continental maps, for the widespread prevalence of traditional peasant farming in Europe prevents the land-use pattern there from changing rapidly. Even then, this information is barely comprehensible on some of the sheets of the French 1/50,000 map, despite a generous use of colour, and is definitely excessive on the all-black German 1/100,000 map, although the draughtsmanship and printing are remarkably fine. On the German 1/25,000 map, however, land-use information is beautifully clear. The two German series should be compared in this respect.

To take another example, the bends and twists of the "rolling English road" cannot adequately be represented on topographical scales, and are generalized even on the O.S. 1/25,000 map. Road widths are greatly enlarged on the smaller-scale maps, the degree of distortion increasing as scale diminishes, for the smaller scales are of particular use to travellers, and other detail is subordinated. In 1945, at the time of the launching of the new 1/25,000 map, there was a certain amount of controversy over the question of exaggerating road widths on this scale. The Ordnance Survey held that exaggeration was necessary in order to make the map of use to the traveller, but critics maintained that it would destroy the advantages of pin-point accuracy on a topographical scale which was one of the major features of the new map.

The Representation of Relief

This is, to the geographer, the most important single function of the topographical map. There are many methods, but most are variants of the three basic techniques of **hachuring, contouring,** and **oblique illumination.** Oblique illumination is in part a survival from ancient maps, where hills were drawn in profile, one side being shaded to give an impression of bulk. The method assumes a light placed close to the surface of the ground in the north-west. All east- and south-facing slopes are therefore in shadow. To-day, this method is seldom employed except in conjunction with more accurate devices.

Hachuring also is a semi-pictorial method. Basically, hachuring consists of a series of parallel lines, drawn at right-angles to the direction of slope and usually of a thickness and intensity roughly proportional to the steepness of the slope. The eighteenth-century cartographer, Lehmann, developed a precise scale of hachuring exactly proportioned to gradient, and a scale of this kind is employed on the topographic sheets of The Netherlands. Some remarkably fine hachuring was employed on the early maps of the Ordnance Survey, though its effectiveness was much greater in lowland than in upland country. The very finest use ever made of hachures was in the Swiss "Dufour" Series. Bad hachuring can be very heavy and ugly. The hachuring of the Austrian General Staff maps—the only available maps for large parts of central and eastern Europe for many years—is bad. Clumsy or inadequate hachures fail to bring out the distinction between steep and gentle slopes, and can never be made to give any precise effect of elevation. The hachuring of the Third Edition of the Ordnance Survey of Ireland is a good example of feeble hachuring which is largely ineffective.[1] The very worst form ever taken by hachuring is the so-called "hairy caterpillar"—a ridge shown by a heavy, smudgy, overcrowded mass of hachures, inaccurate and meaningless in itself and obscuring all other features in the neighbourhood.

Hachures can be combined very effectively with other methods, as will be shown below.

Hill shading is merely a tone shading of intensity proportional to the degree of slope. The principle is the same as in hachuring, and hill shading is often used in place of hachuring on smaller-scale maps. Very frequently it is combined with oblique illumination to give a good plastic impression of relief.

For potential accuracy, no method of relief representation can equal the **contour,** a line passing through points of equal elevation. Its apparent scientific accuracy has dangers, however, for many contours convey an impression of precision which they do not in fact possess. On O.S. maps, for example, only the 50-ft., 100-ft., 200-ft., to 1,000-ft., 1,250-ft., 1,500-ft. contours are actually surveyed on the ground. The others are interpolated from spot heights and sketches, and are of a much lower order of accuracy than the instrumental contours. The same criticism is true of the intermediate contours drawn on the new provisional 1/25,000 series, which are seriously inaccurate in places. In the new resurvey of Britain, now taking place, all contours will be instrumentally surveyed.

The contour interval—the vertical distance between contours—is of the greatest significance in the value of a map. A map having contours 100 ft. apart may miss many significant landscape features altogether. On O.S. 1/63,360 maps of the Fourth Edition, and later, the interval is 50 ft.; on the new 1/25,000 map it is 25 ft. The French and Swiss 1/50,000 maps both employ contours at a 10-metre interval, while the American Geological Survey normally employs an interval of 20 ft., decreasing to 5 ft. in some low-lying areas such as the Mississippi delta, and to 1 ft. in part of the Texas coastal plain. A remarkably detailed and vivid impression of relief can be gained from a closely contoured map, and the very clear picture of physical features obtained makes this series one of the best in the world for the study of geomorphology.

Some of the most artistic results are obtained from combinations of two or more of these methods. The O.S. 1/63,360 Fifth (Relief)

[1] See Sheet 169, used elsewhere in this book.

Edition, first published in 1929, employed contours at 50-ft. intervals, together with buff hachuring and a grey overprint to the hachures on the south- and east-facing slopes to give the effect of oblique illumination. There was also **layer tinting** in buff, the tint changing at each 500 ft. The result was a very effective map, but it did not appeal to the public and was never completed for more than a small part of the country. Some of its finest sheets were in south-east England, particularly in the North Downs area, and one or two very beautiful special sheets were issued for Scotland, such as the Oban and Cairngorms Sheets. This latter map employed brown hachures and brown tinting, and provided a remarkably beautiful and effective map of wild and spectacular country. Unfortunately the whole series is now out of print.

The Ordnance Survey also issued a number of 1/63,360 Tourist Sheets during the inter-war period, of special areas, and usually employing contours in brown at 50-ft. intervals, layer colouring in green and brown, and hachures in brown. These, though effective, were less attractive than maps of the Fifth (Relief) Edition. One of the present Tourist maps is discussed below.

The Swiss 1/50,000 is perhaps the most effective of all maps in the representation of relief. Contours at 10-metre intervals are in brown, except for blue on ice and permanent snow, and black on scree. In addition, this series is characterized by remarkably good **rock-drawing** on broken rock slopes which are too abrupt to be represented by means of contours. Rock-drawing here reaches its finest development —that on British maps is very poor by comparison. In addition, the Swiss map employs a faint brown hill shading, with a grey overprint on the southern and eastern slopes, except where ice occurs, when blue is substituted. The draughtsmanship is impeccable. This map should be studied most carefully as a very fine example of cartography.

The relief of the land may also be depicted by means of **point elevations.** On O.S. maps these fall into the three groups of trigonometrical points, bench marks, and spot heights. Trigonometrical points are stations in the triangulation of the country. Normally they are found on hilltops commanding a wide view. They appear on the ground as concrete pillars having a metal tripod-rest on top and a bronze plate carrying a bench mark let into the side. The elevations of the bench marks are known exactly. Bench marks at other places are elevations of the second order—usually marked in a wall or gate-post. They are usually one or two feet above the surface of the ground. Spot heights are mere points on the map, usually strung along roads, and they provide a useful guide to the form of the ground between contours, of particular use in interpreting the existence of river terraces and/or erosional flats. Those actually shown on the map are a mere fraction of the total number available on the original survey.

The Representation of Cultural Features

In their broadest sense, the features of occupance cover the whole landscape of settled lands. The very form of the woods, and in some areas the details of the stream courses, are the product of man's work. Although the "cultural overlay" is as complete as the surface of the land which underlies it, the object of cartography is not to represent the whole, but to select those elements of the overlay which are of greatest significance to the user of a topographical map, and to represent them in such a way that their pattern is clear, without obscuring the details of the underlying relief. In great urban areas the cultural overlay is the whole map, and here in many cases the representation of underlying relief is greatly subdued. On the O.S. 1/25,000 map contours are shown by broken lines in built-up areas, while, on the Tourist and Fifth (Relief) Edition maps of London, hachures and tinting were largely omitted, and relief was shown by contours only. Thus the whole of the Crystal Palace ridge, to quote an example, disappears from all but the closest scrutiny.

Upon the success or failure of the cartographer in the task of properly representing the cultural overlay in balance with the physique depends most of the value of the map for the purposes of geographical interpretation, for the cultural patterns must be both clear in themselves and clear in their relationship to the underlying terrain if correlations are to be understood and the basic purpose of map interpretation achieved.

The topographical map was, and is, intended primarily for military purposes, and must represent all those features which have military significance. Thus buildings, roads, railways, and field boundaries of all kinds are included wherever possible, and in as much detail as the limitations of scale will allow. Different policies have been adopted on this point by the different national surveys: the Ordnance Survey has been slow to represent field boundaries on its topographical scales, and did so for the first time on the new 1/25,000 map in 1945.

All other features of the map, however, including the emphasis placed on the classification of roads and trackways according to the traffic they will carry, and the extra significance given to prominent buildings, spring from a military origin, even though the maps have been adapted to the needs of the walker and tourist.

Of first importance in the representation of cultural features is the nature of the symbols employed. Ideally, **cartographical symbols** should be self-explanatory, requiring no reference to the key. Many symbols show in plan the features which they represent, for example the symbols for buildings of all kinds, and for bridges, roads, and railways. Others, such as the symbols used for pylons, windmills, lighthouses, and (on many maps) for trees, are drawn in profile. This practice marks the persistence of a venerable tradition: such symbols are usually retained on modern maps only for particularly prominent objects.

A very large range of symbols is employed on the modern map. The increasing use of maps by travellers has led to a great development in the representation of routeways. Railways are usually classified according to number of tracks, and roads are now very fully classified in respect of width and condition, or according to an official classification adopted by the transport authorities. Guide- and mile-posts also are frequently marked. Many foreign surveys attempt much more detail than does the Ordnance Survey.

Appreciation of cultural representation on maps demands careful study of the characteristic sheets of the major national surveys and of representative maps. In this way only can the student acquire that full and wide knowledge of the different methods employed on which enlightened appreciation and comparison may be based.

Non-landscape Features

Names, boundaries, and the classification of land by **administration or ownership** are the principal non-landscape features commonly represented on topographical maps. In general, the relative importance of these features increases with the scale of the map, for on the larger scales there is both more room and greater need for that class of information which is of use particularly to the indoor map reader. The characteristic sheet of the O.S. 1/2,500 map includes fifteen different administrative boundary symbols with fourteen corresponding styles of lettering for use in naming places and districts, while eight further styles of lettering are employed in naming topographical features. The 1/10,560 (6 in./1 mile) map uses a similar range of styles, but the 1/63,360 map employs only three styles of boundary and correspondingly fewer styles of lettering. The new 1/25,000 map, which is primarily topographical, attempts a compromise between the two adjacent scales of symbols for non-landscape features, with but indifferent success. Only three styles of boundary are shown, as on the 1/63,360, but the naming of districts and places corresponds more closely to the system on the 1/10,560 than to that of the 1/63,360, with the result that the names of most districts appear twice, once in upright capitals for the place itself, and once in sloping capitals for the administrative area. If there is also a small part of the larger district known by the same name as the whole but requiring separate identification, the name may well appear a third time, in smaller print with lower-case lettering.

In the assessment of non-landscape features one must first consider how far the information provided suits the scale of the map and the type of terrain. Thus the representation of the least significant non-landscape features would be justified in a map of a part of central Australia, but the same detail would be quite out of place on a map of south Lancashire on a similar scale. Just as it is easy to overload a map with such information, it is equally easy to be too sparing. The American Geological Survey maps are grave offenders in respect of omission.

It is important that the information given should have some degree of permanence. The Ordnance Survey has decided against the practice adopted by some continental surveys of giving the population of individual communes by means of a figure on the map. Without frequent revision, this information rapidly becomes out-dated, and must be used with great care.

The method and style of representation vary widely. Some reference has already been made to the common practice of employing different **styles of lettering** to convey different information. On the O.S. 1/2,500 map, different styles of lettering are used to denote counties, county boroughs, parliamentary county divisions, poor law unions, parliamentary boroughs, municipal boroughs, wards, urban districts, rural districts, civil parishes, towns, and districts. Some national surveys vary the style of lettering employed according to the population of the place named, but this is open to the same objection as stating the population itself. A style based on administrative status is better. A wide variety of styles of lettering is possible. The interested reader should consult Captain Withycombe's paper of 1929 (see p. 202), in which the evolution of the present forms of lettering is traced from early times. The modern tendency is toward lighter and more open lettering, and it is a great pity that the international 1/1,000,000 map, with its very wide and varied use of lettering, was designed in the period of heavier styles before the movement of reform was fairly started.

Even now, the lettering employed by the Ordnance Survey on its modern maps (Fifth, Sixth, and Seventh Editions, and 1/25,000) is very slowly and carefully built up with fine steel pens. A practised draughtsman is unable to draw more than twenty names per day. The Royal Geographical Society has introduced a quicker style adapted to quill pens, but this has not yet found favour with official bodies. Style of lettering varies greatly from country to country. In analysing and appreciating its value account should be taken of differing national styles, and also of the age of the map, for the reform movement is not yet twenty-five years old.

There is one further important aspect of names on maps—**spelling.** The modern map user, accustomed to the standardized forms of spelling, might easily fail to realize that these have in many cases been arbitrarily imposed, and are often at variance with a long tradition in which a different spelling, or even a different name, was employed. The modern "Dorking," for example, was for centuries "Darking," while the names of many rivers were taken from the eighteenth-century topographers and not from local custom. In Gloucestershire, the village of "Aston Blank" (O.S. 1/63,360 (New Popular Edition) Sheet 144, Grid Reference 1320) is still known locally as Cold Aston, this being also its name for postal purposes. Nineteenth-century bowdlerizations of local names are almost always enshrined on O.S. maps, perhaps to the detriment of interest. There is also the factor of human error, as where High Barnet Station appears as High Barton Station on Sheet 51/29 of the Provisional Edition of the 1/25,000 map. Such errors as this are usually speedily corrected.

The arbitrary rendering of place-names has far-reaching results. Consider the rendering of Gaelic names in different parts of western Britain. In Ireland, very few Gaelic names are given in their original forms: almost all have been done into a kind of phonetic English which gives rise to frequent absurdities. Welsh names suffered less, while in many parts of north and west Scotland Gaelic place-names are correctly spelt out, even though the Gaelic tongue may have long since vanished. The possibilities and dangers of place-name inter-pretation from maps have been dealt with elsewhere, but it may be well to repeat that the map interpreter should beware of taking the present form given on the map as etymologically correct.

The classification of land according to administration or ownership also falls into the category of non-landscape features. The modern O.S. topographical maps represent, by a clear symbol, all land in the possession of the National Trust, and on the larger scales all public buildings are distinguished in heavy black. Similar conventions are also employed on foreign surveys and are of considerable advantage to the map user.

Margins and Marginal Information

In former times map margins were most elaborately decorated, but in these more austere days they have lost almost all artistic detail. Even to-day, however, there are few maps which are bounded merely by straight lines, without any form of embellishment whatsoever. Commonly, margins are divided according to scale so as to provide an easy means of measurement. The margins also contain reference systems of latitude and longitude, grid or otherwise. Sometimes decoration may still be found.

Margins have the dual function of limiting the sheet and linking it to the next. For this reason some information is carried from the map across its margins, such as road names on large-scale plans, and road and railway destinations on smaller-scale sheets. On some maps, margins are opened where they cut inconveniently across some major feature, such as a city, a coastline, a river, or a main highway. This has been a practice particularly of the French 1/50,000 series. The Ordnance Survey have employed it widely only once, in the special sheets of the Fifth Edition published during the later 1930's.

Again, the margin includes much information of great importance in the proper understanding of the map. The title of the map is normally stated in the upper margin, together with details of the series to which it belongs and its number within the series. Some larger-scale maps carry no title, merely their number. At the foot of the map it is customary to give the scale, usually in all three forms—verbal statement, representative fraction, and scale bar, the latter usually divided in metric units as well as the national units if these are not metric. A key should be given, including the commonest symbols used on a map and also the most obscure. As it is clearly impossible, within the ordinary limited margin, to provide a full list of all signs and symbols employed, a characteristic sheet is usually published separately; but unless a brief key is given the map loses some of its usefulness.

Other information that must be provided includes a north point, with grid north, if any, also shown. Magnetic north is commonly given as at the date of publication, and a statement appended of its approximate variation from year to year. Secondly, the date of survey must be stated. Much that has been written above emphasizes the fact that a map is already out of date when published, and becomes progressively more out of date as time goes on. A note of the date is particularly important in an area of rapidly expanding urban settlement. The dates of any revisions are commonly stated, but frequently the extent of the revisions are inadequately described. Revision may be exhaustive, or it may apply only to certain features, such as roads and railways: a fact of this kind should be stated. If a map has been compiled from several surveys the date of each must be given. Without this the map loses much of its value. Omissions under this head are a common weakness of much private cartography, and of the Provisional O.S. 1/25,000 map which is a reduction from previous 1/10,560 and 1/2,500 surveys, so that parts of any one sheet may have been revised later than others. This is not at present stated on the maps, to their detriment in detailed work.

Thirdly, some description of the grid-reference system, if any, should be provided, and the datum of all elevations should be stated clearly and precisely. The Sixth Edition of the O.S. 1/63,360 map merely states that heights are given in feet above mean sea-level—a datum which has no existence as a single plane for the whole country. The present Ordnance Datum is mean sea-level at Newlyn, Cornwall, that is, all heights are referred to the mean between high and low water observed at Newlyn for a number of years. But the fenland is low-lying with respect to *adjacent* sea-levels. In fact the base-level for drainage at any point is the level of low-water spring tides at the outfall, while "sea-level" from the point of view of the reclamation of land and its protection from the sea is the level of high-water spring tides at each point of the coast. Along considerable stretches of the shoreline of Britain these two levels are more than twenty feet apart, and reach forty feet apart in the upper Bristol Channel. Students unaware of this have interpreted the levels east of Newport, Mon., at 20–22 ft. above O.D., as a raised beach, and are perplexed to find the

25-ft. contour of the 1/25,000 map crossing the tideway of the Severn below Gloucester. These facts are of some significance to the map interpreter, and it is important to note that the topographical map provides no information about them whatsoever. Admiralty charts must be consulted in each case where such a problem arises.

A similar consideration applies to the interpretation of foreign maps. For example, in maps of the Netherlands all heights are referred to the summer water-level at Amsterdam; those in Belgium originate from low water of spring tides in Ostend Harbour; the German datum is referred to a point below Berlin observatory. To correlate the elevations given on the maps of different countries is, in effect, a problem for geodesy.

Final points of marginal information should include the name of the projection used, the origin of any grid system, the origin of the longitude—by no means always Greenwich—and also the price.

Examples of Appreciation

O.S. 1/63,360 (SEVENTH SERIES) SHEET 114, 1954
(BOSTON AND SKEGNESS)

Relief is shown by brown contours at intervals of 50 feet, strengthened at every 250 feet. Point elevations in black include two kinds of spot height; freely distributed on the low ground, they are helpful when it is recalled that they occur inland mainly on embanked roads. Contours for the hilly ground in the north are elaborate enough to suggest accurate survey; they are finely drawn and adequately numbered.

Bright blue is used for water-names, natural rivers, creeks on the foreshore, and the marsh symbol. Canals, drains, and artificial rivers are in pale blue, between double bright blue lines if they are wide. Sea and tidal estuarine water is in dull pale blue. Symbols are provided for quarries, pits, sandhills, cliffs, rocky foreshore, sand- and mud-banks, and accumulations of shingle, the last being omitted from the key.

Cultural information is abundant. Roads are subdivided into seven groups, partly by Ministry of Transport classification and partly by width. Main roads appear in red, secondary roads in brown, and minor country roads in yellow. For farm roads, access roads, and minor roads in towns no colouring is used. Railways are classed in four groups. The bold red cross formerly printed for level-crossings has been abandoned; on this map, the road and rail symbols thin to points.

Churches are indicated in solid black symbols; other town buildings, and houses in the country, are in grey, but outbuildings and isolated barns in country areas are in black. Bus and coach stations carry a red symbol. Information on land use is scanty; apart from items already mentioned, it is confined to stipple for parks, a simplified tussock pattern for rough pasture, a blue cross-hatching in a black frame for glasshouses, a grey pattern of symbolical trees for orchards, and symbols for coniferous and deciduous trees under a green wash for woodland.

Remaining landscape features relate chiefly to service installations and to antiquities. The style of lettering varies among pre-Roman, Roman, and post-Roman antiquities. Service installations listed in the key include three kinds of telephone kiosk, two of which belong to motoring organizations; Youth Hostels are also marked. Masts, windpumps, windmills, lighthouses and lightships are all shown by pictorial symbols.

Three types of boundary appear in black. Finely-drawn and unobtrusive grid lines are in grey. Latitude and longitude are given by linear scales in the margin, and by intersections at 5-minute intervals on the face of the map. Marginal information includes a revision diagram, information about the grid and about the true, grid, and magnetic norths, scale bars, county names, distances to nearby towns off the map, and a beautifully-lettered key.

Lettering on the map itself varies in an obviously systematic but unexplained way. Minor names generally are in sans serif in which all strokes are of uniform thickness; this lettering is clear but not elegant —contrast the small lettering in the key. Use is made of sloping and upright characters to sub-classify features, but the variation, like variation in kind of lettering, is not keyed.

In several ways, this map is far more attractive and far easier to use than the New Popular sheet which preceded it. Its general effect is by far the less harsh, largely because of the free use of quite small lettering and because of the liberal employment of grey. It would be unjust to call the sheet pallid without comparison with other sheets of the same series where great amounts of complex detail have to be shown. Nevertheless, it can fairly be said that the tangle of minor roads in the silt fen is not easily perceptible at any distance in artificial light, while in close-up the map seems overloaded with a not particularly attractive pale yellow. A slightly more solid tint, and narrower lines, might have been better. In rural areas, too, some individual buildings seem unduly large. On the actual sheet used in the writing of this text, the grey plate had failed to register correctly, especially in the north-east.

O.S. 1/63,360 Tourist Map (Lorn and Lochaber), 1959

Since much of what has just been said of the Seventh Series Sheet 114 applies also to this Sheet, attention will be concentrated on the techniques of representing relief, which are special to the Tourist Map.

Brown contours at intervals of 50 feet, strengthened at every 250 feet, are carried right up to the summits. The intermediate contours are so finely drawn that they do not congest the map, yet they are strong and clear enough to be easily read. The strengthening does not produce that oyster-shell effect to which it has led on some past maps. Since the green wash used on the Seventh Series for woodland is here applied to layer-colouring for areas under 100 feet, the woodland tint has been darkened and the tree symbols strengthened, but contours can almost everywhere be read through the darker green with complete ease.

Apart from the partial layer colouring, this map is distinguished by a highly effective use of oblique illumination and by the generous application of rock-drawing. While the rock-drawing is inferior to the best products of Swiss cartographers, it seems to be more varied and more elaborate than on past productions of the Ordnance Survey. In oblique illumination, on the other hand, the Survey has here succeeded beyond praise. The plastic shading ranges, by gradation, from very pale buff to light yellow-brown on the lit slopes, and is purple-brown of varying intensity on the shaded slopes. Summits are in part untinted. Seen from a distance, the map achieves a most convincing three-dimensional effect. In close-up it is no less effective, for the shading has been applied with great care and delicacy, quite small changes in slope or aspect being accurately reflected in changes of tinting.

Although buildings are marked in grey, their firm but finely-drawn black frames make them identifiable. It is, of course, unlikely that the Tourist style would be applied to maps of heavily-peopled areas, so that one possible cause of congestion does not arise. In any event, allowance has been made for the free use of shading, for example in the strengthening of the footpath symbol—on the map, but not, however, in the key.

It continues to be a matter of regret that submarine contours are not shown below the 10-fathom line, that submarine contours are in fathoms while subaqueous contours for freshwater lochs (not keyed) are in feet, and that defects of spelling should recur—Inversanda (9359) should be Inversands. Such deficiencies, however, do little to detract from the fine achievement of the whole map.

U.S. GEOLOGICAL SURVEY, 1/62,500, EDITION OF 1924 (PINAL COUNTY (ARIZONA) CASA GRANDE QUADRANGLE)

The representation of relief is by means of contours in brown at 25-ft. intervals, every fourth contour being strengthened, and by point elevations of three types—triangulation stations (trigonometrical points) and bench marks, both in black, and spot heights, mainly at the intersections of the land-survey lines, given in brown. In addition, sand dunes are indicated by means of a brown-stipple symbol. The impression gained is one of great accuracy, notably on the lowlands. Water is shown in blue, intermittent streams being shown by blue pecked-and-dotted lines and wells by blue circles.

Cultural information is very sparse, partly because of the very low density of settlement in this area. Apart from the classification of roads, black alone is employed. All buildings are shown in solid black, their forms normally being generalized as small squares. Roads appear in fine hair lines, broken in the case of unmetalled roads. Classified through-routes and secondary routes are overprinted in red, and, if in bad condition at the date of survey, are lined with red dots. Railways are shown by hatched lines, with double and single tracks separately distinguished. On the whole, cultural information is definitely subordinated to the relief, and the occupance seems sparser than it in fact is. Detailed examination reveals, however, a clearly and very precisely drawn map of cultural features, of which a very full interpretation may be made.

Non-landscape features also are sparingly represented. Eight forms of boundary are shown, but naming is restricted to the larger administrative units, such as the Indian Reservations, and to more important settlements, such as Casa Grande and Chiu-Chuischu. Individual farms and ranches are not named, nor does there appear on this map the profusion of rural schools that is so marked a feature of maps of the eastern U.S.A. Styles of lettering employed are clear and effective.

A graticule is printed on the face of the map, and it is difficult to separate this at a glance from the section lines which are very clearly marked in black. The margins are plain, and are used for graticule information, scale bars in miles and kilometres, a grid which is not carried across the map, and some information regarding the destination of roads (printed in red). North point, date of survey, projection, and datum are given, the latter rather inadequately. A full characteristic sheet, together with a description of the topographical maps of the U.S.A., is printed in grey on the reverse.

In conclusion, one may say that this is primarily a relief map, second importance being given to land-survey lines and the cultural features being under-emphasized. Close examination, however, reveals a detailed and accurate map of the cultural landscape, on a map which, for relief representation, has few equals among the topographical maps of the world.

Comparison of Map Series

It is customary in cartographical appreciation to refer freely to comparable series of other surveys. The interpreter needs to be closely familiar with such series and their characteristic sheets. In addition to O.S. maps, the major productions of all the national surveys of Western and Central Europe and North America should be studied. In particular, the maps of France, Germany, Switzerland, the Austrian General Staff, and the U.S.A. deserve close examination. The object of this concluding illustration is to suggest lines on which comparisons may be made between maps of different countries on comparable scales, in order to obtain a better appreciation of any one.

At the outset, a brief summary of the characteristics of each map will be given.

GREAT BRITAIN. O.S. 1/25,000, SHEET SO/00, 1948
(MERTHYR TYDFIL)

Relief is by point elevations in black and by contours in brown at 25-ft. intervals, each fourth strengthened. Rough rock, tip-heaps, etc., are given in black, water in blue. Woods are represented by a tree symbol in grey. All major roads, tracks, and footpaths are shown in black, and the classified roads filled in brown. Buildings are outlined in black and filled in solid grey, except for public buildings which are in solid black. Many names are recorded, some providing much industrial information. Almost all farms, factories, inns, woods and physical features, and many antiquities are named. The result is a crowded, but clear, map, the relief being subordinated to the cultural features in closely built areas, but dominating in rural areas.

GERMANY 1/25,000, SHEET 4506 (DUISBURG) 1958
(PART OF NORDRHEIN-WESTFALEN)

Brown contours are thickened at every 20 metres, broken at odd 5 metres, and supplemented by form lines in places at intervals of 1·25 metres. Some waterside slopes are hachured in brown; water is in blue, and woodland is shown by black tree symbols overprinted in green. All other information is given in black. Suburban building is solid black, with gardens in light black stipple and an unobtrusive orchard symbol; congested building is hatched in black, and factories are in solid black.

Both the range of notation and the key are elaborate. Four types of administrative boundary, four types of railway line, and eight types of road (excluding footpaths) are distinguished. Fourteen classes of land-use information are indexed, three of them further subdivided and two others capable of variation: these are all additional to gardens. Nine types of linear feature, not already specified, include seven types of enclosure-boundary. Further symbols, mainly for landscape features, are classed under twenty-nine heads and number forty-three in all, and thirty-four literal abbreviations are listed. The key to water-ways and associated features gives another thirty-odd explanations. Remaining marginal information is equally carefully presented. Free use is made on the face of the map of variations in style of lettering.

NETHERLANDS 1/25,000, NEW SERIES, SHEET No. 25A
(HAARLEM), 1952

Relief is scarcely present in the area represented, except in the belt of sand-dunes in the west. Sand is marked by dull yellow which vanishes under the green wash for woodland; plastic shading for dunes, in a purplish brown, seems to have been applied by air-brush and thus to be rather coarse, although it is likely that the form of the ground is accurately indicated. Black woodland symbols resemble those on the German map, but are even further simplified. Part of the polderland is marked in green, part left blank, without explanation. All water is in a uniform blue.

Most roads are in a rather heavy red, and are prominent for suburban areas where buildings are black. In town centres, roads are left blank and most building cross-hatched in pink. Factories and similar installations appear in black. A notable feature of the key is the provision made for showing dykes, lateral ditches, lock-gates, sluices, and similar structures. Bridges over the minor open drains of the polderland are recorded in great number.

Marginal information includes the graticule, numbered clearly in black, and grid numbers effectively shown in light red.

In a comparison of these three maps, the most striking point is the much greater dependence on fine engraving on the Continental maps than on the British. Fine engraving is a characteristic of German cartography, and by means of it a great deal of information is conveyed with much greater clarity than on the British map, which both attempts less and is less successful. Whereas the grey tone used on British maps is adequate for buildings, it is far less satisfactory when used for woods and field boundaries, which are by no means clear and tend to be suppressed. On the British map, principal emphasis is given to relief and to buildings, the map being at its most effective in areas devoid of settlement or in closely built towns. It is much less effective in settled rural areas and in areas of mixed urban and rural settlement. The almost complete absence of information on agricultural land use on the British map is noteworthy, although the more rapid change of land-use patterns in Britain than on the continent would diminish the utility of such representation.

The Netherlands map, while obviously constructed from a careful and detailed survey, suffers from the traditional emphasis of road-widths in suburbs, where colouring is also heavy. Town centres seem to be suppressed. The map is perhaps at its most effective in open polderland and in factory areas. Variation of lettering is used to good effect, but the range of colour, while superior to that on the O.S. 1/25,000 map, results in a not altogether pleasing combination.

Despite its limited use of colour, the German map is the most satisfactory of the three. It provides a most detailed and exact representation of a wide range of features, and, as comparison of the keys and of the actual maps makes obvious, has a far greater scope than have the other two maps. Slight exception may perhaps be taken to the use of hachures of uniform width (i.e., hachures which do not taper) for embankments and earthen slopes generally, and to the hatched railway-line symbols which cause groups of sidings, and marshalling-yards, to be recorded in congested patches. On the other hand, the type of symbol used is designed precisely to admit the sub-classification of railways which is one of the admirable characteristics of this production. Contours are less prominent than on the British 1/25,000 sheet, but urban features are more elaborately treated.

This comparison makes it possible to indicate some of the means which the various designers have chosen in their efforts to present great quantities of information. The German map, drawn in great detail and with great care, demands equal care in reading. Although there is a great deal of cultural information, represented throughout in black, fine engraving and the limited use of solid black undoubtedly prevent the map from looking overloaded. The Netherlands sheet relies heavily on contrasts in colour. The British map, effectively employing tapered black hachures and black stippling, and using solid black lines for railway sidings and spurs, is effective with much of the industrial landscape. The grey tint for most buildings enables the whole map to be lightened, but grey is too faint for woodland where light green wash would greatly improve the map.

NOTES AND REFERENCES

The style of maps is dealt with, either generally or in particular aspects, in the following works—

G. CHEETHAM. "New Medium and Small Scale Maps of the Ordnance Survey." *Geogr. Journ.* cvii, 1946, p. 211. (An informative discussion is printed with this paper.)

A. R. HINKS. *Maps and Survey.* University Press, Cambridge, 1942. (See Chapters II–VI inclusive.)

ORDNANCE SURVEY. *A Description of Ordnance Survey Large-scale Plans.* 1954; *A Description of Ordnance Survey Medium-scale Maps.* 1955; *A Description of Ordnance Survey Small-scale Maps.* 1957.

E. RAISZ. *General Cartography.* McGraw-Hill, New York, 1948. (See especially Parts Two, Three, Four, Six, Seven, and Eight.)

UNITED NATIONS, DEPARTMENT OF SOCIAL AFFAIRS. *Modern Cartography.* Lake Success, 1949. (Provides an up-to-date map of the status of topographical mapping in different countries.)

J. G. WITHYCOMBE. "Lettering on Maps." *Geogr. Journ.*, lxxiii, 1929, p. 428. (Followed by a useful discussion.)

INDEX